Family Album

FAMILY ALBUM

ANTONIA
RIDGE

London

First Published in 1952
by Faber and Faber Limited
24 Russell Square, London W.C.1
Fourth impression 1966
First published in this edition 1970
Printed in Great Britain
Latimer Trend & Co Ltd Whitstable
All rights reserved

SBN 571 09388 4 (paper edition)
SBN 571 06897 9 (cloth edition)

To

Isa Benzie of London

and

Léo and Léger of St. Etienne

I

Aunt Kate and Mrs. Penny

My name is Durand, Dorothy Florence Durand—
Dorothy after my mother, Florence after Florence
Nightingale, and Durand because my father was
French.

They say there are hundreds of thousands of Durands
in France, rather like the Smiths in England or the Joneses
in Wales. In fact I once had the pleasure of listening to
two Frenchmen sitting outside a café, briskly arguing
about herrings—of all things. And one banged his fist
on the little table before them and roared, "I tell you
they have all the virtues! Moreover, they don't need
state propaganda to convince them of the nobility of
being numerous! Must be millions upon millions of them
swimming about. Herrings! Why, they are the Durands
of the ocean!"

That taught me to think my name was rather unusual
and romantic, I can tell you. But in a way I suppose it
suits me, as I'm not in the least unusual, and nobody has
ever suggested that I was romantic—not even when I
was young. Indeed my Aunt Kate used to declare that
she had never met anyone with a more disheartening gift
for calling a spade a spade.

9

Aunt Kate. She brought me up. I don't remember my father and mother; they both died when I was a baby. Aunt Kate was my mother's only sister—her only available relative, as she used to put it. My father had some relatives in southern France, but as no anxious Durands came rushing over to England to claim me, there was only Aunt Kate handy to hold the baby. And very well she did it, too. I am afraid you are going to be disappointed if you are now expecting a harrowing tale of a misunderstood orphan with sombre, repressed thoughts. Aunt Kate was far too kind and busy a woman to bother about repressing anybody's thoughts, as long as they didn't expect her to drop everything she was doing and listen to them. She allowed me to think pretty much as I pleased, except when I started thinking of reading in bed with a candle stuck in a cocoa tin, or other such dangerous delights. Then she *would* put her foot down. Otherwise we got on together in the most comfortable way.

Indeed when I look back on my quiet, easy-going childhood, I marvel at my Aunt Kate. She was a school mistress, not in the usual elementary school but in an open-air school, the first of its kind to be opened in our town. It stood on a hill some way out, almost in the country. The children used to travel out to it in a special tramcar that was supposed to leave the city centre at eight-thirty sharp but was always delayed by panting young messengers.

"Please, George Harris says he's coming as fast as he can, but he's got a burst blister on his heel."

"Please, Mrs. O'Leary says will you wait for her Lily. She's being sick, but she won't be long."

I always thought it was Lily O'Leary who had the delicate stomach, but years later Aunt Kate told me it was poor Mrs. O'Leary who always felt so sick of a morning, and no wonder either, living as she did, in a state of perpetual pregnancy. Lily, being the eldest, just had to mind the babies till her mum felt she could face up to another day.

As for Aunt Kate's school, that was condemned years ago. I can't say I was astonished, for I have yet to set eyes on a more happy-go-lucky erection. No fine never-mind-the-cost planning there, I can tell you. The boys' lavatory, for instance, leaned economically, and often most pungently, right against the kitchen. There was only one large class-room which served as hall and dining-room as well. Moreover, every child was supposed to have an hour's rest after dinner, so when the weather was bad all the tables had to be slung out into the playground and the chairs stacked crazily up to the ceiling to make room for the camp-beds. And these, and the blankets and pillows as well, had to be raced over from the shed in which they were kept, every child galloping his best to win warm words of praise from Aunt Kate for arriving with bed, pillow and blanket almost dry in spite of the rain, the sleet, or the snow.

But that ramshackle school had something all the fine planning in the world could not have given it. It had Aunt Kate. She loved her job. To her it wasn't just teaching, it was far more. Delicate, sickly children used to come to her school from all over the town, and she would set to work to teach batch after batch of them to enjoy fresh air, and soap and water, and the good plain food cooked by Mrs. Luke in the kitchen—and no vinegar all over it to sharpen their appetites as at home. And being Aunt Kate, she made it all seem rather like a picnic, even the chasing about in the rain with sacks over their shoulders.

We lived just down the road, not five minutes' walk from the school. Mrs. Penny kept house for us. She was a policeman's widow who had brought up five sons of her own, a sensible homely soul who made no fuss whatever of looking after me until I was old enough to go to school. I used to trot behind her with brush and duster and an occasional lick of polish by way of a treat, or else I amused myself as I pleased as long as the garden gate was tied up and the high guard in front of the fire. I don't remember ever being bored or lonely for Mrs. Penny was the best and chattiest of companions. And she knew better than to talk down to a child.

I used to love to hear her tell of the days when she was a little girl, just my size, and lived on a lonely farm in the West Country; and how four times a year, as regular as clockwork, Sam Small, the pedlar, would call and open his pack on the great kitchen table. And there, inside, would be all the familiar things of course—the needles, cottons, tapes, bottles of ink, writing paper, and cakes of soap; but every time, sure as sure, there would be something fine and unexpected as well, something bright and new to dazzle them all—a tea-caddy with roses painted on it real as life, or a length of lilac-print to make a little girl a pinny fit for a princess, or a box with sea-shells all over the green velvet lid—the

very box that still stood on Mrs. Penny's parlour mantelpiece.

"And I'll tell 'ee what we'll do," she would then say.
"Soon as ever I finish these potatoes we'll go and have
a look at it, and that little house our Bill brought back
from Germany."

And I would hear again, in entrancing detail, how Mrs.
Penny's Bill had been a sailor, sailed round and round the
world he had, till he met a nice red-headed girl called
Annie who persuaded him to settle down in a good
steady job in a place called Plymouth.

And presently, when the potatoes were washed and set
to simmer on the fire, we would solemnly rub our shoes
on the kitchen mat and go into Mrs. Penny's parlour.
And there, on the crowded mantelpiece in the middle of
all the photographs and ornaments, stood the china house
from Germany—roof of curly pink tiles, two crooked
gilt chimneys, four little windows made of real glass,
three red steps leading up to the green front door, and
yellow roses blooming all over the rose-pink walls.

Mrs. Penny would invite me to sit down on her beautiful red velvet sofa, and I would watch her open the
box with sea-shells all over the green velvet lid and take
out the end of candle and the box of matches she always
kept inside; and my heart would begin to beat faster and
faster as she struck a match, lit the end of candle, and
set it down, very carefully and slowly, behind the china
house.

Instantly the four tiny windows would glow with
light, and I would sit on the edge of the sofa, gazing and
gazing at this shining miracle, wishing and wishing I

was small enough to climb up those three red steps, push open that green door, and walk inside. Then I would think that I only had to wait long enough, and "they" would come out. I wasn't at all clear who "they" were, except that "they" were altogether beautiful—to match their house, of course.

Then Mrs. Penny was a great one for singing hymns I remember—fine rousing hymns a body could enjoy singing to the Lord. I can see her now, stout, red and cheerful, striking up "Onward, Christian Soldiers!" as she tackled the ironing, or "Fight the Good Fight!" as we whacked the rugs on the clothes-line, she with the carpet-beater and me with the boiler-stick. And on Sunday evenings, for a very special treat, she would teach me to pick out the tunes on the little harmonium in her parlour, especially her favourite "All Things Bright and Beautiful", which we always sang right through in the most spirited way. In fact Aunt Kate used to say we would have done credit to the Albert Hall itself, such was the power and feeling we put into each verse and chorus.

Friday evenings were very special. It was then that my hair was washed with green soap and rain water, and I would sit with a warm towel over my shoulders and watch Mrs. Penny balance our weekly budget.

First of all she would take out the stout pile of clean towels that looked as if they filled all the top left-hand drawer of our kitchen dresser; and there behind, in two tidy rows, would be the purses, Mrs. Penny's housekeeping purses, each one a different shape, a different colour, and dedicated to a different purpose.

She would take them all out and set them down on the table before us, together with a blue pencil and a red exercise book in which she entered every penny she spent. And I would watch as she carefully counted into the green purse the cash to cover next week's meat supply. Then into the long brown purse went the money for three pints a day and four on Saturday from Mr. Purham, our milkman. Into the silvery white one with a blue ship sailing on it went the cash for Mr. Budd, our baker, and into the fawn one decorated with ivy leaves went the wherewithal for all the other groceries.

Having provided for all our daily needs, Mrs. Penny then proceeded to higher and more complicated finance. Into the grim black morocco purse went a shilling towards next winter's coal; into the old red plush purse went sixpence towards somebody unknown but definitely benevolent called Insurance; into the strawberry-pink purse went a regular weekly sum towards the gas-bill; and into the unlovable navy-blue purse went a weekly instalment to satisfy the outrageous half-yearly demands of somebody mysterious and downright ungrateful who never seemed to do a hand's turn in return, and to whom Mrs. Penny darkly referred as "them Rates".

Then at last we would come to the purse I loved most of all, the beautiful soft blue leather one, which Mrs. Penny called "the Lord's purse". Into this she not only slipped a regular weekly sum, but each time she bought a real bargain, the very thing she wanted but for far less than she had planned to spend on it, then into the Lord's purse went one half of the windfall. And from this purse we not only bought and sent away postal orders to help lonely sailor-boys far from home, and poor, dear children up in London with no boots to their feet, but we also bought, for cash down, lavender, packets of pins and kettle-holders from every beggar who came knocking at our door.

When all the purses were replenished and back in their drawer, with the towels stacked neatly before them, Mrs. Penny, flushed and happy, would say, "The dear Lord will always provide, of course, my love, but the least a body can do is to lend Him a hand." And she would make us both a large cup of cocoa with two spoonfuls of sugar in it, and I would sit taking the tiniest possible sips, staving off bed, glowing with warm happy dignity. My hair was washed, the purses were ready, the Lord had provided—but we could look Him in the face. His purse was ready, too.

As soon as I was five Aunt Kate got special permission to enter me on her register, and I began to go to school with her. Some of her friends took a very poor view of this. "But aren't you afraid she'll catch something?" they would ask, darkly sotto-voce which of course, always made me pin back both my young ears and listen hard.

"No," said Aunt Kate. "No. At least not more than anywhere else. No disinfectant like fresh air, you know."

She was right. Indeed she always swore that every time I *did* catch something it was always during the holidays; and it was certainly true that every time school opened, there I would be, skipping along by the side of her, fit and spotless.

Now, of course, I realise how fortunate I was. If I had gone to the ordinary elementary school of those days I would have been cooped up with at least fifty others, all sitting very tamed and still or teacher would have been branded a poor disciplinarian. Whereas the wind came dancing in and out of Aunt Kate's school, and if it wasn't raining or blowing a gale we would drag our tables and chairs out into the garden—and a battered-looking lot they were, too—and we would learn to read and write, with the sparrows hopping about our feet and the leaves of the trees stirring over our heads.

Then the moment we had mastered something important, such as long division or casting-on on four needles, Aunt Kate kindly let us have the honour and pleasure of teaching somebody else. This we did in the most ruthless way, with many a sharp shove and no putting up with wandering attention or any other ungrateful nonsense.

The boys learned woodwork too, which I considered most unfair. A portly gentleman called Mr. Green came twice a week to instruct them, a gentleman of such dignity that we always called him "Sir".

"Sir wants you," we would say, or "Sir says can he have another pot of glue, please?"

Then Aunt Kate didn't believe in children sitting still for long, even in the fresh air. So she would organise festive pea-picking competitions in the school garden, or blackberrying expeditions along the lanes; and on our return we would work fascinating sums about our harvest. I remember quite clearly that I once worked out that my paper bag of blackberries was worth every penny

17

of £1 8s. 9d. I fancy I must have calculated at the rather more profitable rate of threepence per blackberry instead of threepence per pound.

In the winter Aunt Kate would take us out "sticking", picking up dead branches and twigs in a nearby wood, or she would have us all striding and hopping, counting as we went, and we would work sums about all this, too. Oh, there was no end to the lively games Aunt Kate invented for our education. She was, of course, years ahead of her time, but she never realised it. She thought it plain commonsense.

Unfortunately, the moment a child was well and strong again, back he would have to go to his old school once more, always with regret, often and often with tears. And straightway another peaked, listless child would turn up to take his place. This, of course, made life very interesting, for many of these children were right out of the ordinary.

There was Sam Hawkins, for instance. Now his mother positively loved Sam to be in the worst possible health. She often took a tram up to school for the pure pleasure of keeping Aunt Kate up to date with Sam's sufferings.

"And last Sunday, he just couldn't keep a mouthful down all day, could 'ee, Sam?"

"No, Ma," Sam would say, very proud and pathetic.

"Oh, but he's getting on fine now," Aunt Kate would say. "You should see the dinners he puts away up here. Put on seven pounds last month, didn't you, Sam?"

"Ah, Miss," Mrs. Hawkins would swiftly counter. "I've told 'ee before, that don't mean a thing in our family. His poor Dad was all of fifteen stone when he passed away. Took six of them to get his coffin down the stairs."

Then the school doctor, who came once a month, decided Sam would be all the better without his tonsils and adenoids, and he promised Sam's mother to send her a card as soon as there was a bed free for a night in our children's hospital.

That did it. Sam straightway became unbearable. It wasn't only the martyred side he put on, it was the way he bragged rapturously and incessantly about "MY operation" that was so infuriating, especially to those of us with no operation, past or future, in which to glory.

Aunt Kate, however, seemed as deaf as a post when Sam was about, till one day he was discovered, red-handed, chalking "Old Sir Greeny is a fool like a monkey on a stool" all over the lavatory walls. Then Aunt Kate let him have it, and we, of course, listened with the greatest of pleasure.

"And," wound up Aunt Kate, "the next time you get up to any monkey-tricks, Sam Hawkins, YOU WON'T HAVE THAT OPERATION!"

The delighted guffaws that tore up fairly rocked the school. Moreover, from that day on, whenever Sam annoyed us, we promptly echoed Aunt Kate. "All right, Sam Hawkins, now you won't have that operation!"

Sam, who was no fool, soon saw there was no future in operations, and, better still he began to stem his mother's plaintive dirges. In fact, the last time Mrs.

Hawkins came to school it was to complain that Sam was kicking out the toes of his boots playing football. "He's getting that rough, Miss," she whined, "I just can't think what's coming over him."

"Then I'll tell you," rapped Aunt Kate and seized this golden opportunity to speak her mind to the indignant Mrs. Hawkins.

Then there was the Italian boy, Luigi Capaldi—we called him Gee-gee, of course. He was a Neapolitan with a swift dark temper. When he first arrived he thought nothing of jabbing his pen into anyone he suspected of making fun of him; so he was treated with considerable respect, especially when he swaggered in one day in a pair of long black corduroy trousers.

"My!" said Aunt Kate. "Oh, my! You *do* look smart, Gee-gee!"

"Yes, Mees," agreed Gee-gee, all flashing smile. "My Uncle Giulio he goes to preeson for seex years these time, so I gets ees new pants."

Some days later however, Gee-gee missed the school tram and came panting in late, very late, and we all gaped to see that the right leg of his grand new trousers had been slashed off at the knee. As he slouched towards Aunt Kate, the other leg which he had rolled up slid down to his ankle, and there he stood for a moment, one trouser-leg long, the other short. But the murderous scowl on his face fairly froze all the titters, and Aunt Kate, sober as a judge, said quietly, "Hello! Had an accident, Gee-gee?"

"Yes, Mees," gulped Gee-gee. "Up a tree I have accident."

He did not have to add another word. Aunt Kate read him like a book. He had torn the right knee right out of Uncle Giulio's new pants, and his mother, flaming away, had seized the scissors and she had taught her Luigi to climb trees in his good corduroy trousers.

In less than five minutes we were busy with crayons and sheets of black paper, drawing flowers from memory.

Gee-gee, swathed in a blanket, was sitting up in Aunt Kate's high chair keeping a stern eye on us all, whilst Aunt Kate carefully measured and cut off the left leg of his trousers to match the right one, and showed two big girls how to hem them round in real tailor fashion.

Then we all held up our drawings for Gee-gee's inspection, and Aunt Kate pinned the chosen master-pieces on the wall, before we packed up our crayons and set to work to lay the tables for dinner. And I remember how Gee-gee, radiant in his neat corduroy shorts, fairly fell over everybody and everything in his warm desire to be helpful and obliging.

Yes, that was my Aunt Kate. She took everything in her kind homely stride. As she saw it, it was part and parcel of her job, that was all.

But perhaps most gratefully of all I remember how cool and casual she was when people began to look at me and say, "Well! Isn't she growing a big girl! Getting on for eleven, eh? Suppose you're busy now coaching her for the scholarship?"

"Well, I would hardly call it coaching," Aunt Kate

would say; "we just polish up her spelling when we've a moment—eh, Dorothy?"

No, she never once made being eleven seem something crucial, almost sinister. It was the way all her friends talked that gave me a nasty sinking feeling that I was heading straight for something extremely critical, something terribly important.

And thanks to this, one fine day in my eleventh summer, armed with a brand-new pencil-box and Mrs. Penny's best handkerchief with lace all round it, but with my heart in my buttoned boots and feeling quite sick with apprehension, I set out to sit for THE SCHOLARSHIP. That was precisely how everyone spoke of it, in deferential capitals, as it were. Every year our Education Committee awarded forty-five of these scholarships to the brightest and best eleven-year-olds of our town. At least that is what we respectfully believed they did. So the honour and glory of winning one was simply terrific. Added to which, all the proud winners not only went straight into one or the other of our four secondary schools, they also received a few pounds each year for four years towards books and other scholarly expenses.

I'll never forget that day. We tackled the arithmetic paper in the morning, when presumably our young brains were fresh and unjaded. The afternoon session was devoted to English composition. We had the choice of two theses: "Why I am proud to be a Briton", or, "The most exciting day in my life".

I had never given a thought to being a proud Briton, so I had to set down the most exciting day in my life—

the day Aunt Kate took me up to London to see the sights. I gave the exact time I got up, what we had for breakfast, and the precise times to the minute that the excursion train left our station and steamed into Paddington, together with details of all I had to eat on the way.

I wrote off the sights of London, however, in one sentence—"Then we went and had a look at Buckingham Palace and some other places"—and straightway got on with the journey back home, giving the exact time of our departure from the capital, and what was in the sandwiches Aunt Kate had bought in a London teashop, and how there was a little boy in our carriage whose nose would go on bleeding till Aunt Kate made him sit up straight and slid three cold pennies down his back, whereupon he said, "Ooh! Can I keep them?" which made everybody laugh.

Then I remembered, in the very nick of time, that Aunt Kate had said, "And *do* try and end up in an interesting way!" So I thought desperately and wound up with an interesting, "At a quarter to eleven, 11.45 p.m., we caught the tram back to the end of our road. I did not want any supper because I was not hungry. At twelve o'clock, midnight, I went to bed, tired but happy after my most exciting day."

Then, as I still had a few minutes in hand, I printed THE END in very nice red capitals and drew a pretty frame all round it.

Maybe the examiner enjoyed reading time-tables, maybe it touched him the dogged way I plodded through the long-division and practice sums, but a month later, to everyone's undisguised surprise, including Aunt Kate's, there was my name printed in the Scholarship Results in our local newspaper for all to read: Dorothy Florence Durand.

But only by the skin of my teeth, though—forty-fifth out of forty-five.

2

The French Family Album

Early that September, Aunt Kate and Mrs. Penny stood
proudly at our garden gate and waved me off to my new
school, very stiff and solemn in my new blue serge gym-
slip, white starched blouse, braid girdle swung low
somewhere between my middle and my knees, and a
most uncomfortable straw boater anchored on my head
by a piece of thin white elastic that went behind my ears
and under my chin.

And I hadn't worn all this grand new rig-out for more
than a week before I secretly wished I had never won that
wretched scholarship. Everything in my new school was
so different, so dismally different from Aunt Kate's
happy-go-lucky school. There was such a tense atmosphere of urgency about the place. We were forever expected to GET ON. And getting on meant getting our
young noses down to our books. In Aunt Kate's school
there was so much besides books—the garden, the bees,
cross old Billy the goat, and there were always new
children turning up who had to be shown where everything was kept, and that made a girl feel useful and
important. Whereas here, even "break" was bleak and
dull in that dreary asphalt playground with great tall

prefects strolling majestically up and down saying, "Pull up your stockings, do!" and "Tie back your hair," and "Stop that shouting!"

Then one day Miss Williams, who took us for French, picked up my new exercise book and said, "Durand! Why, that's a French name. Are your parents French?"

"Only my father," I said.

"Then I *shall* expect *you* to get on," she said. "What does your father do?"

"Nothing," I said. "He's dead."

I suppose it was my matter-of-fact voice, but instantly every head turned to stare at me, and Miss Williams, very taken aback, said, "Oh! Dear, dear! I *am* sorry." And there was a terrible shocked silence. But I couldn't have been more sharply aware of what she was thinking, of what they were all thinking. I could just hear them gasping, "And she sounds as if she doesn't care either!"

And I realised with a queer sort of surprise that it was true what they were thinking. I didn't care. I just didn't care. I had never even thought about not having a father and mother, not with Aunt Kate about. I'd never even bothered to ask questions about them. I'd been too busy —just being happy.

And there I was—shown-up, and in front of all those girls too, a queer sort of orphan if ever there was one.

A great lump came up in my throat and I pinched my knees hard; I tugged my garters and let them snap back hard on my legs—anything to keep back the tears. Not because I suddenly felt sorry for myself. Oh no! I hated being made to look different, so heartlessly different, that was all.

We had apple-tart and cream that afternoon for tea, and I stolidly got through my usual substantial two helpings, and gave no sign whatever that anything was wrong till I had plodded through all my homework.

Aunt Kate, I remember, was sitting in front of the fire with her knitting and the evening paper.

"Aunt Kate," I said, and I didn't look at her but began to draw feathers on my blotting-paper. "Aunt Kate, what was he like—my father, I mean?"

"Your father?" said Aunt Kate, very surprised. "Well he was very nice-looking—at least I thought he was. Dark eyes and hair, and he had a way of waving his hands about when he talked."

"Go on," I said, and suddenly my voice came out very queer and high. "Go on. Tell me all about him. And her, too. I want to know everything, everything! Please, Aunt Kate."

Aunt Kate looked at me. "Of course I will, love," she said gently. "Of course I will. In fact I was only thinking last Sunday that now you're such a big sensible girl I ought to give you something I've been keeping for you."

She put down her knitting, went to her writing-desk, unlocked the bottom drawer, and lifted out an album, a thick heavy photograph album. I had often admired similar ones on other people's parlour tables—the handsome covers, the brass clasp, the glossy pages with handy cut-out spaces in which to slip the photographs, all about which trailed delightful hand-painted sprays of lilies, pansies and forget-me-nots.

But written on the cover of this one, in tall gold letters, was "Album de Famille".

27

"Oh!" I said. "French!"

"Yes," said Aunt Kate. "It was your father's. Let's have a look at it, shall we?"

I pulled my chair up close to hers, and suddenly it swept over me—the strange feeling I used to get when I was small and I would sit on Mrs. Penny's sofa and watch the little china house her Bill brought back from Germany. And with my heart beating very hard and fast, I watched Aunt Kate unfasten the great brass clasp and open the album.

There, on the first page, all set about with pink and blue forget-me-knots, were the photographs of two fat babies, and on the top of the page someone had written in queer pointed handwriting, "En souvenir des dix mois de Marius Alexandre et Mariette-Louise Durand."

"There you are," said Aunt Kate. "There's your father, Marius Alexandre, and his twin-sister, Mariette-Louise, at the nice plump age of ten months."

My father at ten months looked disappointingly like any other fat baby, except that he had nothing on and was lying on his stomach, modestly half-buried in a thick fur rug.

But his twin-sister, Mariette-Louise, now she looked a very French ten-months. She wore an entrancing little chemise trimmed with lace threaded with ribbon—that is, she had one arm in her chemise and the other outside. Aunt Kate said she considered this most artistic, for we could admire the fine tucks, the lace, and the bow on her right shoulder and yet see for ourselves how plump and dimpled she was by her bare left shoulder. More delightful still, Mariette-Louise wore a fine chain round her neck with a medal hanging on it, on each of her fat wrists was a bracelet, and there were tiny pointed ear-rings dangling from her little ears. And whilst my father was glowering savagely down at his thick fur rug, Mariette-Louise facing the world in her smart chemise, was kicking up her toes, and beaming away, showing all six of her new teeth, as if to say, "Don't I look wonderful!"

There was something so gay and rollicking about her that I laughed out loud—for the first time that day; and Aunt Kate, chuckling too, turned over the page.

There was the funniest photograph I have ever set eyes on. It was far too large to slip in any of the spaces, so somebody had glued it in place. It showed forty little children arranged in four rows, ten to a row. The first row sat on the ground, the second row sat on a form, the third stood behind this form, and the fourth row perched high and triumphant on a long plank set on two chairs. And somebody had obviously ordered them to fold their arms across their chests, for an obedient, attentive few had managed to tuck their hands under their armpits. But most of them seemed to be anxiously clutching their middles. As for the rest, they simply had not heard the word of command. Far too busy staring at the camera.

Across one corner of this fascinating photograph, in the same pointed writing, it said, "Marius et Mariette-Louise à L'Ecole Maternelle".

"Now there," said Aunt Kate, "is as lively a class of Mixed French Infants as a teacher could hope to meet. Only they seem to call it the maternal school over there, and not a bad name for it either.

"You see that cross little boy scowling in the front row—yes, that one with the cross on his chest. That's your father.

"And that dear little girl with the cross on her pinny, that's young Mariette-Louise, his twin-sister."

My father, dressed in a long-sleeved check overall, was sitting cross-legged on the ground, hair cropped short all over his round head, hands clenched on his stomach, looking as black as thunder.

But Mariette-Louise, also in a check overall, her curly hair topped with a fine butterfly bow, was perched on the plank in the back row, positively hugging herself with joy.

"Now this," said Aunt Kate, "was your father's favourite photograph. He used to say that for one whole morning he fairly wore himself out trying to be a good quiet boy so as to have the honour and glory of standing up there on that plank. And when the great moment crawled round at last, sure enough, there he was, proud as Napoleon, up on the plank with nine other hand-picked infants. As for Mariette-Louise, she hadn't even tried to be good, so she was very properly seated on the ground, well in view, where even she couldn't get up to anything.

"Now the photographer, according to your father, was a dark mysterious type at least eight feet tall, and he suddenly bent in two, and both halves disappeared under a great black cloth. Everybody held their breaths and their stomachs. All at once your father could stand the suspense no longer. He let out a yell, jumped high in the air, and down crashed the plank and all that back row of best infants.

"And his teacher and the eight-foot photographer, blazing away at the top of their voices, yanked out that Marius Durand and dumped him on the ground in the very front row. Worse, far worse, they set giddy young Mariette-Louise up in his place on the plank in the back.

"And your father used to say it wasn't this degradation to the ranks he minded so much. No, no, it was the thought of all the shining hours he had wasted, sitting still, trying to be a nice quiet boy, that rankled so."

As Aunt Kate turned the page, the laughter died on my lips, and I caught my breath. There was my father again; there was no mistaking him. But now he was about my own age, eleven or so, wide-eyed, very solemn, and very grown-up in a dark suit with long trousers, white waistcoat with round pearl buttons, stiff white collar, very big white bow-tie, beautiful handkerchief pulled well out of his breast-pocket, large prayer-book in one hand and a pair of white gloves in the other. And high on one arm was a wide satin ribbon tied in a great flat bow, long ends edged with a heavy silk fringe hanging down to his wrists.

By his side stood Mariette-Louise, very solemn too, in a beautiful white dress right down to her toes, long sleeves and high neck edged with fine lace, rosary in one hand, prayer-book in the other. But more lovely to me than all beside, she wore a wreath of white rose-buds on her head over a long lace veil that fell in a cloud about her to the hem of her frock, but caught back at the temples to show her smooth dark curls and serious little face.

"Why, they look as if they're going to be married!" I said.

"No," said Aunt Kate. "That is how they dress French children for their First Communion. It's a most solemn and special day in their lives, by all accounts."

"Don't . . . don't turn over yet," I begged.

"Right," said my Aunt Kate. "You have a good look, love."

She placed the great album on my knees and picked up her knitting. And there I sat, looking and looking, my heart very warm and proud to see such solemn beauty—and in my very own family, too.

And it must have been the flickering fire-light of course, but it seemed to me that the boy who was my father looked up at me with dark anxious eyes as if to say, "You *do* like us, don't you? Please, please, say you like us!"

"Oh *yes*," I said, "oh yes!"

And suddenly, out there in the little hall, the grand-father clock struck a solemn nine, my bedtime, and no argument ever allowed.

But there was no need for me to look imploringly at Aunt Kate. She knitted on as if she had not heard, and presently she got up and put more coal on the fire. And I could hear Mrs. Penny talking to the cat as she locked up for the night, and as she went up the stairs her cheery, "Good night, me dears! Don't 'ee sit up too late now!" seemed to echo from another world.

It was then that I turned over the page, and Aunt Kate looking up, said, "Ah, now that was where your father lived when he was a boy." And there was a photograph of a little hotel. On the wall over the door in a flourish of fancy letters it said:

Marius Durand

CAFÉ-RESTAURANT DES MONUMENTS DE NÎMES.
CHAMBRES POUR VOYAGEURS.

Aunt Kate said my father had told them that it was a smallish place where travellers could get a good meal, a bottle of wine, a cup of excellent coffee, and a comfortable bed for the night, as long as they did not expect carpets and a bathroom thrown in as well.

But what really interested me was that on the pavement outside this little hotel were half a dozen little tables. At one of these tables, a tall bottle and a glass in front of him, sat a stout jovial-looking gentleman with a straw hat on the back of his head, a thick watch-chain stretched across his waistcoat, and carpet slippers on his feet.

"Now that," said Aunt Kate, "is your grandpa, Marius Durand, waiting for the travellers. Your grandma was probably inside washing-up or making the beds."

"What does 'des Monuments de Nîmes' mean?" I asked.

"The Monuments of Nîmes," said Aunt Kate. "They lived in Nîmes in the South of France. It's a very ancient city, by all accounts. Your father used to say that there are monuments still standing there that were built by the Romans themselves. And a great arena where the gladiators used to fight."

But I was not very interested in the Romans and their gladiators. On the next page I had spotted a most remarkable photograph of a plump smiling lady sitting on a rustic bench, holding a fan, and wearing an enormous hat with a whole bird sitting on it, and a stiff dress with great leg-of-mutton sleeves.

By her side stood a soldier, a most magnificent soldier, holding a very long sword, so long that both his hands were folded on its handle at his waist and the point rested on the ground between his spurred boots. At his elbow stood a tall table with a cushion on it, and on this cushion was his helmet, a beautiful feathery streamer hanging from it.

"There you are!" said Aunt Kate. "There's your Grandma Durand all dressed up and with her best hat on. And no wonder she is looking so proud, because that is your father by her side. Yes, that is how he looked when he was doing his military service. He was in the 30th Regiment of Dragoons. You can see the thirty embroidered in white on both sides of his collar. And he used to say it was a thousand pities the photograph wasn't in colour, because he looked absolutely superb—tunic very dark blue with snow-white facings on sleeves and collar; twenty-three silver buttons that shone like twenty-three full moons or his sergeant-major would have had his life; beautiful bright red trousers with a narrow piping of dark blue down the sides; and leggings and spurs that made the passers-by blink.

"And his helmet there on the cushion, that was made of some silvery metal too, and that long feathery streamer was a fine sweep of black horse-hair that used to dangle down their backs. And that's a little plume of scarlet feathers trimming up the front, but they were only allowed to wear that on a Sunday—the red feathers in front, I mean.

"And that isn't a sword, my dear. Your father used to get quite indignant if we called it his sword. It's a sabre. The French cavalry always wore sabres, and waved them heroically as they charged into battle.

"And your father used to say that waving them heroically, sitting on a horse, was dead-easy compared with walking round with the darn things on Sundays and their nights out. Now that did call for a cool nerve, he could tell us, especially if a man doted on dancing. A pretty girl in her best frock and her senses, always thought twice—if given the time—before she got up to dance the polka with a poor devil of a dragoon bristling with spurs and one hundred centimetres of sabre.

"Then you see those smart white kid gloves tucked so artistically between his hands? The photographer kindly lent him those. And your father used to declare that it was a thousand pities that he hadn't had the courage to borrow his captain's horse for the occasion because that aristocrat wasn't called Emperor for nothing, and he would have rounded off the picture very stylishly.

"He said this was their walking-out uniform of course. They didn't look nearly so dashing behind the scenes in their barracks. As for their pay, that was a sou a day, just about a ha'penny a day if you please, which meant fivepence every ten days. And out of that some brigand would stop three-ha'pence for their tobacco, which left them exactly threepence-ha'penny to squander every ten days.

"And now let's take a look at this," went on Aunt Kate. She turned the page, and there was a photograph of two elegant young women sitting side by side on a velvet couch. Their hair was tightly frizzed all over their heads, they had the smallest of waists, and their dresses swept the carpet at their pointed feet. One had a bunch of roses on her lap, the other held a book. Behind them stood two stiff young men in tight jackets and high starched collars. And yes, one was my father; I knew him by his eyes. The other was thinner and taller, with a fine waxed moustache.

Aunt Kate told me that this was taken the day Mariette-Louise, sitting there with the roses on her lap, became engaged to the tall thin young man with the fine moustache. Aunt Kate said she was sorry but she couldn't for the life of her remember his name. As for the other young woman, the one with the book on her lap, now she was more or less booked to get engaged to my father later on. Her name was Alexandrine and she was Mariette-Louise's best friend. And it seemed that everybody approved of this arrangement, especially my Grandpa Durand. Alexandrine had a nice bit of money tucked away and she could cook like an angel—a French angel, of course. As for my father, well, he thought he might as well please the whole family and marry Alexandrine as anybody else.

Then it was decided that he should go to London for a few months to learn English so that when my grandparents retired he and Alexandrine could take over the

Café-Restaurant des Monuments de Nîmes and have "English spoken. Tea as in London" in gold letters on the window.

There was, however, precious little money left over by the time my father had paid his fare to London, so he found a job as fourth chef in a great West End hotel, where he swore he spent twelve hours a day dancing apprehensive attendance on the first chef, a vitriolic gentleman from Marseilles who let fly with ladles and everything else handy every time the fourth chef dared to offer him the wrong knife, or failed to come flying on the wings of the wind at his every yell. More disheartening still, all day long every soul in the kitchen spoke French and never, never, under any circumstances did they stop to make tea as in London.

And all my father yearned to do on his night out was to sit down, preferably with his boots off; but he sternly decided he ought to make an effort at least to listen to some English whilst he *was* sitting down, so he joined an evening class where students of both sexes could improve their minds at half a crown a subject.

And there, sitting next to him as he battled with English literature, was a slip of a girl who had come up to London to study music. My mother. And that, said Aunt Kate, was that. Definitely that. They just looked at each other and fell head over heels in love.

It seemed it took my father a whole long purgatory of a week to compose two letters: one to Alexandrine, the other to his father.

Alexandrine wrote back by return of post, positively enchanted at the news. In my father's absence she, too, had been swept off her feet, by a Spaniard, a most romantic señor who bred horses in Morocco. And now she could say "Oh yes!" with an easy conscience to her ardent Spanish admirer, and she wished my father all the happiness in the world with his English miss, and she would forever remain his old playmate and friend, Alexandrine.

But the pen of my Grandpa Durand positively scorched the paper on which he wrote back to my father.

"Return at once!" he blazed. "Alexandrine will get over this Spaniard, and you will do your duty and forget this English girl. Have you taken leave of your senses? Have you forgotten that Alexandrine has so handsome a dowry tied safely up in Government bonds? Remind yourself how she can cook! Are you going to allow this Spaniard to carry off so desirable a wife?"

But the Spaniard did marry Alexandrine, and my father married my mother. And from that day on, not a line, not a word, did he receive from his family. Sadder still, all his letters came back—unopened.

"He was very upset, of course," said Aunt Kate. "But he and your mother were very happy together. Look, here they are, on their wedding-day."

She turned the page, and there they were—my father and my mother.

Even now I don't know whether I want to laugh or cry when I look at this photograph. My father was so anxious to please his English bride that he went out and bought himself the very oddest wedding-suit—a thick tweed, very horsey check, four big patch pockets, tight belt, knickerbockers ending just below the knee, thick woollen stockings, and stout laced boots. And in one hand he carried a great flat tweed cap.

Aunt Kate said he felt a regular John Bull in this rig-out and no mistake.

My mother, however, looked very elegant. She wore a long velvet dress trimmed with row upon row of silk braid, a long feather boa round her neck, and a tiny bowler hat with a great bunch of violets curling over the brim.

But I always forget all this when I look at their faces. There is something about them that never fails to make me catch my breath. They look so young, so happy, so very much in love. I know I was only a child when first I saw this photograph, but even then I knew that this unknown father and mother of mine had been happy, most radiantly happy.

And as I looked and looked at them, I heard Aunt Kate say, "Well, my dear, that's the lot, I'm afraid."

It was true. The rest of the great thick album was empty. And Aunt Kate did not have to tell me, I knew that my father and mother had wanted to fill all those fine glossy pages, those empty waiting spaces, but there had not been the time, not even for one of me.

"Aunt Kate," I said, "how did they die?"

"An accident," said Aunt Kate, and she told me how she had gone up to London for the Christmas holidays the year I was born to have a look at me. And one evening my father, as merry as a cricket, said, "Now us, we will make some hay while the sun shine! Aunt Kate is here to survey our little Dor-o-tee, so we will go to this panto-mime!"

They never came home. A terrible street accident. They were walking along, hand in hand, when it happened.

"So I took you home with me," said Aunt Kate. "What else could I do? And I wrote to your Grandpa Durand at the Café-Restaurant des Monuments de Nîmes, but the letter came back, 'Unknown at this address'. So I wrote to the British Consul. I sent money to put advertisements in the local papers. But nobody replied. Oh, I did everything I could. I wanted to make sure I was doing the right thing keeping you, even though I didn't want to part with you . . . heaven only knows why, young image that you were, waking poor Mrs. Penny and me at crack of dawn, yelling away to all the neighbours that we were starving you!"

Aunt Kate laughed, but her kind blue eyes were full of tears.

"Dorothy," she said, "I didn't tell you all this before; I thought it best to wait till you asked. But sometimes it worried me. I thought maybe I ought to talk to you, that it was all wrong that you didn't even know what your own mother was like."

"But I did, Aunt Kate," I said. "I did. She was just like you, of course."

Aunt Kate blew her nose very hard. "Well," she said, "that's about the very nicest thing I shall ever have said to me."

She kissed me, and, without another word, she raked out the fire, put the guard in front, and we turned out the gas and went upstairs to bed.

And under my arm I carried my Family Album.

3

The China House

I remember reading somewhere that "Memory ever gilds the past". But I'm not so sure. My memory never casts a golden glow on the years I spent in the secondary school for instance, or on the undistinguished way I plodded on, never drawing attention to myself in any way, always safely and inconspicuously wedged in the middle of everything from hockey and rounders to term examinations.

Except in French. I simply slaved to be top in French. In fact Aunt Kate used to declare that if I didn't look out I'd end up by being able to do everything in French, except, of course, speak it. But that is how we learned it in those days, as if it were a dead language with a very stiff written examination at the end of it, so no nonsense about wasting valuable time trying to speak it.

But secretly, to me French meant more than that. Far more. There was also my Family Album.

Every night I would sit up in bed and have another long look at all my photographs. Even now I could tell you every detail, every button, every ribbon.

Presently, as I looked and looked, I would slip into a queer world of make-believe all my own. I always began by saying a polite "Bonjour" to each photograph in turn, but under my breath, of course. I didn't want Aunt Kate or Mrs. Penny to hear a big girl like me talking to herself.

And I would pretend they all answered back. "Ah! Bonjour, Dorothy, bonjour!"

I would then try out some more French on them. "Ecoutez," I would say. "Ecoutez, s'il vous plaît." And I would pretend they all listened with the greatest pleasure as I rattled off my new French verb or something else I'd learned for homework that evening.

But if it was something very hard, or so deadly dull that it had taken me all my time to master it, then I always turned to the photograph of my Grandpa Durand sitting at his little table, taking it easy outside the Café-Restaurant des Monuments de Nîmes. And I would recite it all to him.

And carried away by this feat of scholarship, my grandpa would whisk off his straw hat and shout, "Ah, bravo! Bravo, Dorothy, bravo!"

I would then cash in on this shining victory and say, "Ecoutez, grandpère; you don't mind now, do you? About my father marrying my mother and not Alexandrine I mean?"

"Ah non!" my grandpa would roar. "Certainly not! Not after hearing you say that verb! Mais asseyez-vous, mon enfant; yes, that's right, sit down. You deserve a glass of wine!"

And I would sit down at his little table and he would call to my Grandma Durand and she would leave the beds and the washing-up and come hurrying out in her best dress and the hat with the whole bird on it. And she would kiss me on both my cheeks and say she would have recognised me anywhere, but anywhere! And my grandpa would pour me out a whole glassful of wine—rhubarb wine because that was the only kind I knew about.

And as I sat there sipping it, down the street would gallop three children all in long-sleeved check overalls— my father, his twin-sister, Mariette-Louise, and her best friend, Alexandrine. And they would pull up sharp, I can tell you, to see me sitting there drinking rhubarb wine as cool as a cucumber. But my father, being a boy, would straightway begin to show off. "Ici, vous!" he would say. "Regardez!" And off he would go, walking on his hands, or turning double somersaults as clean as a whistle.

Then, by way of a change, I would make them all grow up, and now they would come sedately down the street, first Mariette-Louise and Alexandrine, hair tightly frizzed all over their heads, daintily holding up their long silk dresses, and behind them, arm in arm, my father and the tall thin young man with the fine moustache, the one who was engaged to Mariette-Louise. And I would invent long conversations in which all was most carefully explained and most piously forgiven just as in the last chapters of the Christian Lady's Novels, which I always read from cover to cover when Mrs. Penny left them about.

I would then bundle Alexandrine straight off to Morocco to wed her true Spanish love, but I would marry Mariette-Louise to the tall thin young man in the very greatest style with six sorts of sandwiches, a trifle, and a three-tiered cake. And when we had waved them off in

a "fiacre" with an old shoe tied on the back for luck,
I would make my Grandpa Durand turn to my father,
the repentant tears streaming down his face, and choke,
"Allez! Return to England and marry your English Miss.
And bring back your daughter Dorothy to be the sunshine
of our dear Café-Restaurant des Monuments de Nîmes,
Chambres pour Voyageurs."

Oh yes, I invented the very grandest conversations—in
English, of course, but sprinkled all over with every
French word I knew. But I always kept the best, the
loveliest part, to the end.

I would pretend that I was just about to start on a
second glass of rhubarb wine when down the street would
gallop my father on a real Arab steed, a blood brother
to Emperor and considered by many to be the finer of the
two aristocrats. My father, of course, would be in his
best walking-out uniform, the horse-hair on his helmet
streaming behind in the wind. And I'd make it a Sunday,
too, so that he could wear his plume of red feathers as well.

And he would draw smartly up in front of me and
wave his long sabre and cry, "Bien! Très, très bien! I was
hoping I should find you here. I'm off to be decorated
by the President again. So drink up your wine and jump
up behind. Dépêche-toi, ma fille!"

And I would gulp down my rhubarb wine and jump
up behind, and off we would go, clop-clop-clippetty-clop,
faster and faster along the cobbled streets, till we came
at last to a vast square. And there before a great cheering
crowd, the President would be waiting for us; and with
bells ringing, flags flying, brass bands playing, he would
kiss my father on both cheeks and say that France was

proud of Dragoon Marius Durand, and pin yet another medal on his chest.

Oh, there was no end to the medals and glory and fine Arab horses I heaped upon my father, not to mention the expensive white kid gloves I lavished on him, so that he need not borrow from kind photographers any more.

One thing, however, may seem strange to you. I never pretended anything at all about the last photograph in my album, the one of my father and mother on their wedding-day. I will tell the sober truth. I was afraid to. Afraid that if I made them come to life they might go away and never come back again, as they did that night when they went to the pantomime. So I left them where they were, safe and happy in their photograph; and I looked and looked at them. And loved them. But that was all.

And this will show you how little any of us knows what goes on in the mind of a child. All the while, everybody, even Aunt Kate, thought I was a stolid, most matter-of-fact child. Indeed more than once my school report said: "English. Making steady progress but lacks imagination."

Moreover I went on making steady progress and lacking imagination, and any girl who went on doing that, in that school, in those days, progressed straight towards one career and one only—teaching. I know it sounds fantastic, but that is how it was. Only the rare, the enterprising spirit ever dreamed of branching away and taking up nursing or sitting for some Civil Service examination. So nobody thought it in the least remarkable that the whole Sixth Form of my year took up teaching to a girl. Even less remarkable, there was I, firmly wedged as usual, in the middle of them. Indeed I can most truthfully say I became a teacher because it never entered my head that I might do anything else; because that is what everybody expected me to do.

As for the two dreary years I spent in a training college, well, I might just as well have been still in the secondary school. There were, if anything, even more finicking rules and regulations. Those in authority plainly considered they could trust us no farther than they could see us. Heaven alone knows why, for it would be hard to gather together a more tensely conscientious band of young women, who meekly accepted that theirs was not to make reply, theirs never to reason why, least of all why our lecturers dwelt so passionately on how NOT to teach and so vaguely on just how to teach.

So I cannot say I was full of joyous confidence when I started on my first job—the babies' class in the mixed infants' department of a large elementary school in the poorest quarter of our town.

I was supposed to teach fifty of these babies, all between three and four, in a classroom designed to hold thirty-five infants—and static ones at that. These seemed to churn round and round me, a bewildering sea of little faces. The first few days I marked the register and prayed for the best, because everyone of those fifty babies obligingly chimed "Yes, teacher" to any name they fancied. As for trying to count them! Well, one day a worried-looking woman burst in and said, "Oh, Miss, have you seen my Alfie? He's only two and I've lost him and the milkman said he fancied he saw him going to school with that Florrie Edwards. Why, Miss, there he is! Oh, Alfie, you bad wicked boy!"

And yes, there was Alfie, squashed into the back row, and I had not even noticed the bad wicked stranger in our midst.

I hadn't been there a month before the Headmistress summoned me to her desk in the hall. She came straight to the point. "Miss Durand," she said, "in your own interests, and most certainly in mine, the sooner you forget all the high-falutin nonsense you seem to have learned in your training college, the better.

"The noise coming from the babies' room these days is beyond free expression—it is howling mutiny. You simply must have real discipline. The next time they begin to get out of hand, make an example of one of them! Glare at him! Quell him with a look! And if that doesn't work, call me in, and we will see what a good hard smack will do."

That afternoon I accordingly stood and glared with all my might at a happy young rascal called Bertie Toogood, and that wasn't the right name for him, I can tell you. Bertie bore it for a time, tossing his head, and pretending he hadn't noticed me. Then he began to shuffle his feet, and at last he went very red, took a deep breath, and exploded, " 'Ere, you stop it! Stop that gawking at me, or I'll tell our ma. She'll learn you to be rude! Staring and staring!" And to my dismay he burst into noisy tears.

I did not apologise, but I felt like it.

That evening, as we washed up the supper things, I began to say I might as well give up teaching; I'd never be any good at it; and that I was sorry, of course, after all Aunt Kate had spent on me.

Aunt Kate, however, began to chuckle, then hastily said she'd hate to appear unsympathetic, but, to tell the truth, the desperate look on my face had set her thinking of "Miss Primrose and the Horse".

Now "Miss Primrose and the Horse" was one of Aunt Kate's favourite stories, and I never grew tired of hearing her tell it. But that night it no longer seemed just one of Aunt Kate's funny stories. It suddenly became consoling, comforting.

Aunt Kate, like most teachers of her time, began teaching at the ripe age of fourteen—pupil-teachers they were called. They taught all day and got through their examinations in their free time. Miss Primrose was Aunt Kate's first headmistress, and a very frost-bitten primrose she was, too. Aunt Kate said she did better than just rule with a rod of iron, she carried the nasty thing about her—a vicious little cane hooked in her belt. And she hammered nails with large brass heads exactly so far apart all over the floor of the hall; and when the children marched in for morning devotions each child had to come to a halt with its heels precisely so, covering its appointed brass nail. Then as poor ailing Miss Prendergast struck up "New every morning is the love" on the piano on the platform, Miss Primrose, cane in hand, dodged smartly in and out between the ranks giving vicious little cuts on every lawless pair of legs that had dared to shuffle off its nail.

Then she would stalk on the platform, wave majestic-ally to poor Miss Prendergast, and they would begin their devotions with "Rejoice today with one accord", and with each pair of heels well and truly riveted on one brass nail.

Once, when poor Miss Prendergast was away ill, with something well-nigh fatal or she wouldn't have dared to stay home, Miss Primrose ordered Aunt Kate to play the hymns. And Aunt Kate was putting all her young soul into "Onward, Christian Soldiers!", leading them against the foe in the most spirited way, when Miss Primrose suddenly breathed down her neck and fairly froze her on her stool.

"Teacher Kate," she hissed, "kindly remember you're playing a Christian hymn not a heathen polka!"

On her fifteenth birthday Aunt Kate was placed in sole charge of Standard O, which she said was a kind of concentration camp for the backward in the draughtiest corner of the hall. Miss Primrose, among many other injunctions, sharply directed Aunt Kate to get every girl through all the first twelve pages of their nice new reading-book before she herself examined them at the end of the month.

Now this new reading-book was called *The Animal World*. On each page was a picture of an animal, together with a few remarks about its appearance, its usefulness to man, and any other endearing qualities.

And Aunt Kate said she got down to that *Animal World* with vigour and determination. Poor backward Standard O plodded their weary way through those first twelve pages time and time again till Aunt Kate could recite the lot with her eyes shut.

She didn't know it, but so could Standard O.

Came the great day. Pupil-teacher Kate handed Miss Primrose a nice clean copy of *The Animal World* and stood by, waiting for the compliments.

But that Miss Primrose ordered Standard O to open their books at page sixteen. Yes, SIXTEEN, if you please. And there, staring them in the face, was that unfamiliar beast, the Zebra.

Standard O eyed this stranger to their Animal World, and sensibly decided to stand no nonsense from *him*. So up got the first girl and began:

"*The Horse*. This is a picture of the horse. The horse is a noble animal. The horse is the friend of man. The horse is clean, obedient, and willing."

Pupil-teacher Kate gulped. Miss Primrose's cold eyes nearly popped from her neat little head. "Sit down," she said. "You go on, Lily Grant."

Lily Grant went on.

"The horse works from dawn to dusk for the farmer in his fields. He pulls the trams along our busy streets."

"Sit down," snapped Miss Primrose. "Now you, Florrie Davies."

But Florrie Davies, and every girl of Standard O, stuck stoutly to the guns, and recited the praises of "The Horse", as on page six, to the undeserving picture of "The Zebra" on page sixteen.

Then Miss Primrose closed her book and turned her icy glare on poor Pupil-teacher Kate. "I thought I told you to teach them to read twelve pages, not *recite* them," she rasped. "One thing is crystal-clear. You will *never* make a teacher!"

But Aunt Kate did make a teacher, a teacher in a

thousand. And that evening I did as she suggested. I sat down and wrote to our Director of Education and asked for a transfer to a senior school. "You'll get on better with older children," said Aunt Kate. "And listen, Dorothy, while you're at it why not point out how well you did in French? It may lead to something. You never know!"

Well, maybe it did, for within a month, to our delight, I was offered a post in a new type of school that had recently opened close-by—a central school which catered for girls between eleven and sixteen.

The headmistress, Miss Clarkson, straightway put me in charge of Form 1C, and Aunt Kate and I had a quiet laugh over this, because my Form 1C was not unlike Aunt Kate's Standard O. They were the eleven-year-olds who had just managed to scrape into the school, but only just. And it was my job to polish them up till they were considered bright enough to join up with the others of their age.

And no sooner had I made a start on all this than there was a big change at home too. Mrs. Penny still kept house for us, as brisk and cheerful as ever but getting a little deaf and more than a little absent-minded. I'll never forget the evening I met her on the way to chapel, carrying the kettle, the small black kettle she liked to keep at the ready by the side of the kitchen fire.

"Bless me soul!" she gasped. "Then I must have put me old handbag on the fire ready for your tea, me dear!" She had. It was blazing merrily away when I rushed in.

Then, to our great sorrow, her Bill, down in Plymouth, lost his wife after a sharp and bitter illness. They had no children, and as Mrs. Penny put it, poor Bill missed every hair of his Annie's head. "He do just sit and grieve," she said. "I dunno what'll become of him, I'm sure!"

"Mrs. Penny," said Aunt Kate, and took her hand, "you feel you ought to go down there and look after him, don't you?"

"Yes, me dear," choked Mrs. Penny, "I do."

A fortnight later Aunt Kate and I saw her off to Plymouth. She leaned out of the train, the tears streaming down her dear old face. "God bless 'ee both, me dears," she said. "And Dorothy, I've left 'ee something on the parlour mantelpiece."

When Aunt Kate and I came home, we went into Mrs. Penny's parlour, now so bleak and bare. And there on the mantelpiece, looking very forlorn, was the little china house, the one her Bill had brought back from Germany. Stuck between the crooked chimneys was a note:

"DEAR DOROTHY,

"I know you was always set on this. So here it is with my dear love to remind you of the dear old days when we used to sing 'All Things Bright and Beautiful' together, which happy hours I shall never forget, and I hope neither will you.

"With best love to you and your dear auntie and mind you look after yourselves.

"AMELIA PENNY."

When I turned round, there was Aunt Kate half crying, too.

"Well, we are a pair," she said. "Come on, let's have a cup of tea."

That evening I took the china house up to my room and put it on my chest of drawers by the side of my Family Album. And there it stood for many a long year.

It is very hard to explain why a woman treasures such things.

I have sometimes been amused to hear a smart young thing say, "Oh, Mummy, *must* you keep *this* on the mantelpiece!"

"Put that down," Mummy will rap. "Why, I've had that since I was seven. Your Uncle George gave it to me when I was in bed with the measles!"—or some other sound reason for keeping whatever it was.

I don't think we ever put the real reason into words, even to ourselves. But these odd treasures are maybe the only key left to us, the only thing that can unlock for a moment that golden world of fantasy where once everything was just as we wanted it to be.

At least that is how I felt about my china house, now standing there by the side of my Family Album.

4

For Lo, the Winter is Past

We missed Mrs. Penny terribly, of course. As Aunt Kate said, there just aren't enough Mrs. Pennys to go round in this sad world. But we rubbed along as best we could with the fitful help of Mrs. Justin—her Rosie went to Aunt Kate's school.

Mrs. Justin had optimistically offered to oblige daily with the housework, and Aunt Kate used to sigh that she didn't mind so much paying Mrs. Justin for all the days when she could not oblige, but she did resent the masterly way we were always hypnotised into feeling so very sorry for Mrs. Justin as we got on with the work ourselves.

If it wasn't Mr. Justin in rip-roaring trouble again because he never would learn when he'd had enough, then it was one or the other of the children raced off to hospital in an ambulance, in the very nick of time, with all the bells ringing and the policemen holding up the traffic, or something else very dramatic.

Mrs. Justin, complained Aunt Kate, liked everything so very hot and strong, her troubles as well as her tea.

But all this was nothing compared to the black trouble

that lay before us. I noticed that Aunt Kate was coming home from school looking tired and pale, and very worried, which was most unlike her. She said her eyes were troubling her. Put it down to her age, of course. In those days every ailment of a middle-aged woman was always immediately set down to her age, and God alone knows how many women endured endless misery thinking it to be their natural and inevitable lot.

But I managed to persuade Aunt Kate to see our leading eye specialist. He was very kind but blunt. He thought Aunt Kate was going blind.

At first I could not take it in. It could not be true, of course. Not blind! Not Aunt Kate! O God, I prayed, not Aunt Kate, not Aunt Kate!

But I heard myself quietly asking if we might have a second opinion.

He arranged everything for us; the very next week we went up to London to see a most eminent oculist. He, too, was kindness itself. I could see that he hated telling us, but we had to face it. Aunt Kate was slowly going blind, and nothing, simply nothing, could be done about it.

Even now, after all these years, I cannot bear to think of the aching misery of the next few months. One day in particular I shall never forget. It was one of those warm shining days we sometimes get in late April. I happened to look out of a bedroom window, and I saw Aunt Kate standing in the garden, her face upturned, straining to catch the blue of the sky, the gay froth of blossom on our old cherry tree—for the last, the very last time. And I could see her lips moving, and in my heart I knew what she was murmuring—the lines she loved to teach the children to say at that time of the year.

For lo, the winter is past,
The rain is over and gone;
The flowers appear on the earth;
The time of the singing of birds is come.

I turned away, my throat so tight and dry I thought I would choke.

But perhaps hardest of all to bear was the brittle brightness between us, the thin ice as it were, with which we strove to hide the cruel depths of our anxious grief.

It was almost a relief when Aunt Kate broke down one evening. She said she had always planned that I was to spend most of what I earned on myself. She had so wanted me to enjoy my life, see something of the world, meet people. She said she had always hoped that when we had saved up a little I would go over to France for a while; maybe I would come across some of my father's relations there. "I just know they would be glad to see you," she said. "I just know they'd be kind and generous, as he was."

She said she did so wish now that she'd had the sense to save more, that she dreaded the thought of being a responsibility, a burden.

"I couldn't bear that," she wept. "Oh, I couldn't bear that!"

I didn't interrupt her; I let her talk, say all she had in her mind. Then I kissed her and said I asked for nothing

56

more than to open the door when I came home of an evening and see her there.

And this was true. It was a privilege to live with my Aunt Kate, especially in the days, the years that followed.

I gradually arranged the house so that she could find things safely and easily. She began to crack little jokes again, saying that for the first time in her life she knew where everything was. She began to teach herself Braille; she did most of the housework; and more moving to me than all beside, in her closing darkness she patiently taught herself to garden.

She had always loved to potter round our garden where she had planted many an old-fashioned favourite. Now every scented plant, every sweet-smelling bush became doubly dear—the daphne that always flowered just after Christmas; the wallflowers that obligingly sowed themselves year in year out and all from a penny packet of seed bought when I was a baby; the purple lilac that grew by our garden gate; the jasmine that bloomed all through June and July; and the ivy-leafed geranium that flowered all the summer long, pungent and sweet, against our kitchen wall.

Then there were our two great untidy lavender bushes before which tidy gardeners would groan and wring their hands and offer urgent advice to which Aunt Kate always turned a deaf ear, saying lavender bushes were old-fashioned parties like herself who didn't take kindly to gadding about. She loved to grow mignonette, too, and violets in a special spot where the early morning sun would catch them, and night-scented stock that opened wide under the stars and filled the air with quiet sweet-ness. And from June to August she never missed picking her daily posy of pinks, calling blessings on the head of that dear Mrs. Sinkins, wherever she might be.

But best loved of all was the lemon verbena, at least that is what we called it, a graceful bush that grew to the right of our front door. Aunt Kate would carefully snip off a little spray for honoured visitors and say, "There! Keep that between your handkerchiefs, my dear. There's nothing half so delicate and sweet." And she would tell how she had reared it from a little slip that Bill Penny had brought her home, wrapped in a damp dishcloth, all the way from Greece where it grew, so he said, wild and free for all to pick.

Yes, Aunt Kate grew to love her garden most dearly. I can see her now, face suddenly bright, sniffing the air and saying, "Bless me! Old Homer has come out since we had breakfast. I can smell him from here!" Old Homer was a rose tree, another old-fashioned party, and worth a dozen of his more high-falutin relatives, or so Aunt Kate used to swear.

And maybe it was my fancy, but it always seemed to me that no garden could be quite so scented, so full of faithful old friends, so eager to respond to gentle groping fingers that did everything but see.

During the winter months Aunt Kate knitted endlessly and, as she liked to boast, most economically—I often found her knitting away in the dark. And it amazed me to see how she learned to remember quite intricate patterns, especially for the soft lovely shawls she delighted to make for new babies.

Yes, my Aunt Kate gradually filled all her darkness with kindly homely service, and she never expected anyone to feel sorry for her. Indeed people often used to say, "It does me good to have a cup of tea with your Aunt Kate."

Aunt Kate's greatest joy, however, was the way she was remembered by the children she had taught. They used to call with little presents long, long after they had left school. I shall always remember opening the door one evening to a smart young man in a pearl-grey suit and a flashy tie with a diamond tie-pin stuck in it.

"How do, Dorothy," he said. "I heard your auntie wasn't too good, so I've brought her a bottle of O-dee-Cloan, real high-class stuff; she'll like this all right. But you don't recognise me, do you? I'm Sam, Sam Hawkins, now-you-won't-have-your-operation Sam. Remember? Mind if I come in?"

Aunt Kate was delighted to talk to Sam. It seemed he was getting on a fair treat, in business on his own, open-air job, too, we'd be pleased to hear—selling jellied eels outside race-courses near London.

"And I'll tell you what," swaggered Sam, "I'll give you a red-hot cert for the three-thirty next Wednesday. You both put your Sunday skirts on Fresh Air Filly. Just your cup of tea, eh?"

Oh yes, very jovial and breezy, our Sam Hawkins now. And very warm-hearted. He took to calling on us regularly, never without some thoughtful little gift that he thought Aunt Kate could enjoy; never without a good story that she enjoyed even more.

"Went to the Labour Exchange the other day," Sam

remarked one evening. "Always believe in keeping me eyes open for a gilt-edged job. And there was a chap in there I know, called Mike, waiting to collect his unemployment. Now this Mike, he'd do for one of them adverts: You too can have a body like mine! Six foot three of him if there's an inch, and size seventeen in collars if he ever wore one which he don't.

"And the nervous little chap behind the counter gives a nervous little cough. 'Hem!' he coughs. 'We've had a letter signed—er—British Justice. Mentions you, Mr. O'Leary.'

"'Is that so?' says Mike, suddenly very savage.

"'About that new job of yours down at the panto-mime,' hurries on the little chap, and if I'd had me hat on, I'd have swept it off to him, because it's plain that he's hinting that Mike had better think twice before holding his great hand out and swearing he hasn't had the chance of a stroke of work since last he called.

"And Mike's no mug; he cottons on, too. But the look on his face says he'd like to meet British Justice one dark night to thank him for taking such an interest in him.

"'Scene-shifting, I suppose?' hurries on the well-meaning little chap.

"Mike leans over the counter, all six foot three of him, and he cooes, 'Och no, Mister! I'm one of thim fairies, thim dear little fairies!'

"Then he straightens up. 'Put that in yer book, Mister,' he roars, 'and the back of me hand and the sowl of me foot to British Justice!'

"Laugh!" guffawed Sam. "I nearly cried."

And so, of course, did we. Yes, Sam was a born talker, and we were a most appreciative audience, so a first-class time was had by all when Sam called in of an evening.

Then there was Luigi Capaldi, the Italian boy, the one we called Gee-gee. Now his family had made a modest fortune in their little restaurant—ice-cream in summer, fish and chips in winter—and they had all gone back to Italy. But every Christmas Aunt Kate received a handsome card with flowers embroidered in real silk on it, and on the back would be "Merry Christmas, dear Miss and Dorothy, also Happy New Year from Luigi Capaldi, your Gee-gee of the velvet pants who forgets you never".

So the years went by, uneasy years of peace, dark years of war when Aunt Kate knitted sea-stockings as if she alone was responsible for fitting out the whole British Navy. From time to time she would renew her attempts to persuade me to go off for a holiday, without her, but by and by she gave up the tussle.

Then the central school changed its name, it became a secondary modern school, but year in, year out, my job did not change. I went on teaching one Form 1C after another. At times Miss Clarkson would almost apologise for this, and wind up with something soothing and complimentary about the way I brought them out, and "nobody could understand them so well" and other gratifying words of praise. The harsh truth was, of course, that nobody else on the staff wanted the job. The children who went into Form 1C went there because they weren't considered bright enough to go anywhere else. But I could never forget that I was always considered a dumb sort of child, too, with no imagination, and I suppose it helped. In fact I used to get a great deal of quiet pleasure keeping my own little records of children who were graded 1C at the age of eleven and who did just as well as anyone else when they left school, sometimes better.

I am not going to pretend, however, that I didn't indulge in a good grizzle from time to time, and say I wished I had the luck to be in charge of children who practically taught themselves. But I honestly don't think I should have liked them better. It always seems to me to be such cruel nonsense to blame a child for not having a gift for book-work, about as kind and intelligent as blaming him for having straight hair or blue eyes.

I cannot say, however, that I ever thought seriously of the future. Say what you like, most of us have precious little time or inclination to sit down and consider what life is doing to us. We just get on with it.

At least that is how it was with me. Until one morning —the twenty-first of December it was, and bitterly cold. I went into Aunt Kate's room with an early cup of tea. She was sitting up in bed in the warm blue dressing-gown I'd given her for her birthday, propped up with pillows—she always liked three—her knitting in her hands.

Dead. She was dead. My Aunt Kate was dead.

And it had been as she had always prayed it would be . . . kind, homely. She had been turning the heel of a sock for Mrs. Penny's Bill.

And on the table by her side were the presents she had made for Christmas, all tied up . . . and labelled.

When the day came for me to take up my ordinary life again, I came home late from school—I had stayed behind to do some marking. I let myself in, put a match to the fire and set the kettle on the stove for a cup of tea. And I wondered miserably if the house would always feel like this—empty, chilly. And I ran upstairs to get a cardigan.

When I opened my bedroom door the moonlight was streaming through the window, right on the little china house Mrs Penny had given me and my Family Album.

And if ever you have known what it is to feel desperately tired, lonely, unhappy, you will know how you stretch out both hands to any memory that brings warmth and comfort. And I sat on my bed—I hadn't switched on the light—and the long years rolled back and I lived again that night, the night Aunt Kate gave me my album. I seemed to hear her dear homely voice, her warm kind laugh. And suddenly I knew what I was going to do. I don't know whether I thought it, or whether I spoke aloud, but "I'll go to France," I heard myself say. "Yes, of course, I'll go to France."

And I picked up my Family Album; and it opened at the photograph of my mother and father on their wedding day. Maybe you remember I tried to tell you how happy they looked.

Well, that night in the moonlight, they seemed to shine.

And strangely comforted, I put on my cardigan and went downstairs. And the kitchen was full of steam and the kettle dancing, white-hot and empty, on the stove.

At the end of the month I handed in my resignation. I gave two months' notice, as I knew Miss Clarkson would like the time to find another experienced teacher. But, bristling with surprise, she gave me to understand that I was not only behaving in the most peculiar way— I was also downright inconsiderate—upsetting her time-table like this, and after twenty-three years' unbroken harmony between us, too!

Everybody else, however, simply took it for granted that I was sensibly taking a long holiday and improving my French whilst I was at it. I suppose Miss Clarkson slowly came round to this way of thinking, too, for one afternoon she said, "Oh, Miss Durand, can you give me any idea when you expect to return?"

"No," I said. "No. I'm afraid not. Depends how far my money goes."

"Well," she said, very bright and forgiving, "when you *do* return, and I just cannot believe that you won't come back to us, not after all these years, I really must try to give you a rest from Form 1C. I am hoping to be able to arrange for you to take French literature and conversation right through the school!"

And she beamed on me as if she were offering me all this and heaven too. So I didn't have the heart to say anything except, "Oh, thank you, Miss Clarkson. That would be nice."

I felt a humbug, but how could I explain, and to her of all people, that I had no plans, no plans at all; that in some queer way I didn't want to make any plans; that I had no fixed ideas of what I was going to do when I *was* in France, much less what I wanted to do when I had to return.

Everybody else, however, seemed to know precisely what I would do.

For instance, I was at my desk one afternoon waiting for Form 1C to straggle in from their weekly cookery lesson, when I heard two of the senior girls chatting outside my open window. I couldn't help hearing what they said as they strolled past.

"Fancy good old Dorothy D. going off to France!" said one. "France! Of all places!"

"Oh, I can just see her," said the other young woman, "stooging round museums and places, improving her mind. They always do."

At that moment Form 1C poured in. And I don't know, I suppose I was feeling out of sorts, but I looked at them and thought I had never tackled such a lot—thick-headed, unresponsive. . . .

To make matters worse, there was an exasperating outburst of note-passing that afternoon.

"Don't be so mean! You said I could stand between you and June, you know you did"—"Lend me your comb"—"Mind you give your extra threepence to Pat," and other peculiar messages.

And I thought that here I had been, slaving away with them, ever since September, and they couldn't be less interested, couldn't care less. And I began to think bitterly of all the long years I had put in, slogging away with one Form 1C after another. "Ah well," I said to myself, "it all goes to show, it all goes to show. . . ."

Strangely enough, it did; but not what I thought.

When I walked in on my last morning in school, there they all were, in their seats waiting for me. "Well," I said, very taken aback, "you are bright and early!"

"Yes," they agreed, and turned to wave urgently to Patricia Bingle. She stepped out and said, "Please, Miss Durand, we thought you would like this, to remind you of us." And she held out a large photograph.

As I took it, I felt hot with shame. That afternoon, that very afternoon when they had exasperated me so, passing round notes, they had combed their hair, titivated themselves up and gone to a professional photographer to have this photograph taken. For me. For ME. There, across one corner in red ink, was written: "For Miss Durand with love from Form 1C." And on the back they had all signed their names.

But that was not all. Out walked June Smith and heaped still more burning coals of fire on my head. She held out a large parcel done up in pink tissue paper and tied with silver string.

"Please, Miss Durand," she said, "we all hope you will have a nice time over in France, and be ever so happy over there, and . . . and . . . oh dear . . . well, please this is from us all, all of Form 1C, with our best wishes and love."

She shot back to her seat, and they all clapped. And I stood there, photograph in one hand, pink parcel in the other—speechless.

"Oh, do open it," they urged. So I opened it, and there inside was a very handsome handkerchief satchet of bright pink satin trimmed with a sky-blue ribbon rosette. Inside were six pink handkerchiefs, embroidered with a large blue D.

And under the satchel was a big box of chocolates, a very big box, and no ordinary one either. Its lid was a framed picture, real frame, real glass—Dante meeting Beatrice.

Heaven only knows how much it cost them, or how many sweet coupons they sacrificed. Indeed it must have been so costly that it had been in the shop a very long time, far too long, for when I opened it that evening— and thank heaven I didn't do it in front of them—every chocolate was white with mildew.

I can't explain it, but this moved me even more. And I went up to bed that night feeling happier than I had done for many a long day.

5

Journey to France

I have to laugh now when I think of the way I cleared
off to France. It was almost comic. Everyone was so sure
that I would go "stooging round, improving my mind"
that I was showered with suitable addresses, mostly in
quiet cathedral cities. "Now this will suit you down to
the ground," I would be told. "Very nice place, run
especially for English visitors, so no horse meat or any
of that sort of thing; and only ten minutes from the
Hotel de Ville, fourteenth-century you know, and a tea-
room right opposite where you can get quite a nice cup
of tea."

And I would pocket the address and say, "Oh, thank
you so much!" and feel positively guilty that I felt no
enthusiasm, no inclination whatever for the painstaking
sight-seeing so clearly expected of me.

Then I wrote to Mr. Stevens, our landlord, with whom
we had always been on the best of terms, and asked if his
nephew was still looking for a house, as I had decided
to go to France for a while. When I arrived home from
school that evening, there they were, Mr. Stevens, his
nephew, and his nephew's wife, all waiting for me on
the doorstep.

By eight o'clock we had settled everything. Young Mr. and Mrs. Stevens were not only delighted to take over the house, they positively jumped at the chance of buying most of the furniture, old-fashioned as it was. It was also agreed that I was to keep one room, furnished, which young Mrs. Stevens would keep dusted and aired whilst I was away.

"Just so that I may feel I have somewhere to sleep when I come back, but only till I have time to look round," I assured them.

"Oh, but we'd love to have you!" cried young Mrs. Stevens. "Wouldn't we, Bert?"

Bert said yes that they would. And I said, well, we'd see.

I don't think they even noticed how vague I was about the future, they were so full of rosy plans themselves. They raced up and downstairs, looking lovingly at every room, every cupboard, eyes shining, clearly overjoyed to think that they were to have a place to themselves, a home of their own. And young Mrs. Stevens came running back as I was closing the garden gate behind them. "Miss Durand," she said, "I simply must tell you. It's going to be heaven, really it is! You see, we were at our wits' end. We're paying the earth for those two furnished rooms and we didn't dare to tell them, but we're expecting a baby, and now, oh . . . !" And she flung her arms about me and kissed me.

Four weeks later I stepped into a taxi with two brand-new suitcases, a large green one and a small brown one, and set off for France. But the wind did not stand precisely fair for me; on the contrary, it was tearing and howling along the streets in the most disquieting manner.

And I sat in the train heading for Dover, thinking, "Well, Dorothy F. Durand, you're a fine one! Where's your common sense? No plans! Nothing booked! And sitting here feeling so pleased with yourself!"

It was true. There I sat, a warm, eager excitement mounting in me, feeling almost as I used to feel when I was a child and I would sit and watch Mrs. Penny's little china house, quite sure something lovely was going to happen. I only had to wait long enough.

And why not? I asked myself. Hadn't I listened, spring in, spring out, to Form 1C reciting how Mr. Wordsworth had once wandered lonely as a cloud and lived to be very glad he did? Well, I was going to wander round France, and gather a host of French memories that in the years to come would "flash upon that inward eye which is the bliss of solitude", or so the poet swore. And I hoped he was right, for I saw plenty of solitude ahead, and next to no bliss. Moreover, it was most unlikely that I would ever again be able to afford so long a holiday to wander where I pleased.

Then I looked up at my two new suitcases on the rack opposite me, and one half of me apologised to the other half. I admitted that if I'd had any sense I would have packed this, that, and the other, all of which I would probably need at some time or another. Whereas, up there in my large green suitcase, swathed in two cardigans, was my Family Album; yes, yes, my great heavy Family Album. Not to mention the outsize chocolate box with Dante meeting Beatrice in a nice heavy framed picture on the lid. I had turned out the chocolates, though— stuffed it with stockings instead.

Nor was this all. Up there in my sensible small brown suitcase under my bright pink handkerchief satchel and wrapped in a thick woollen scarf was another odd travelling companion—the china house, the little china house Mrs. Penny had given me, the one her Bill had brought back from Germany.

"And very peculiar you'll look," went on the sensible half of me; "oh, very peculiar you'll look if you are faced with one of these thorough-going Customs officers and he tips all this out and sets it in a line on his counter. Very amusing that will be, won't it?"

But I need not have worried. To begin with, the wind dropped, so that the Channel rippled smooth and kind as a lake in summer. I found a comfortable sheltered bench on deck, pushed my suitcases under it, and was pulling a scarf from my coat pocket, when out fell a leaflet I had picked up in Dover, the one officially handed out, I'd noticed, to all foreign visitors to our hospitable shores. "Welcome to Britain" on the pink cover. Page one: Currency and Customs Regulations. Page two: Food Rationing, Identity Cards and Police Registration.

I was thinking that somebody might have tried to think up a warmer welcome than that, when a voice said politely in French, "Please, Madame, is the rest of the bench taken?" And there stood a rosy-faced little nun clutching a black leather valise, a bulging black string bag, a gentleman's umbrella, a black woollen shawl, and a very big bundle of plants carefully wrapped in damp newspapers.

"Oh no!" I said, and moved up a little. "Do sit down."

71

"Thank you, Madame," she said as gratefully as if the bench belonged to me and I had made her a present of half of it. And she sat down beside me, still clutching all her luggage. So I asked if she would like me to stow some of it under the seat with mine, and she said, well, no, everything was quite comfortable except perhaps the plants. Now if I could stow *them* somewhere safe, she would indeed be glad, but please not where they might drip on any of my things.

"They are for my parents' grave," she said. "Very fine perennials, as you can see, Madame."

"Yes," I agreed. "They certainly are."

"They will be so pleased," she went on. "Papa will be ninety on Saturday, and Maman eighty-eight next December."

"Really!" I said, not knowing what to make of this.

"Yes, Madame," said the little nun happily. "It is a very good age, isn't it? And in my Order, we are permitted to return to our homes when our parents are too old to look after themselves properly."

"Very kind and sensible too," I said, and began to see daylight.

"Yes, Madame, it is most kind," said the little nun. "It means that they know I shall now be able to stay with them until the good God calls them."

"But the perennials?" I asked.

"Oh, I shall plant them in the garden for the time being," she said, "where Papa and Maman may see them from the window. They are very strong young plants. Sister Marie-Benedictus chose them specially for me. She has told me just what to do. She looks after our

72

convent garden, you see. She knows everything about plants. Oh, Papa and Maman will love them, especially the daisies. Such bright, pretty colours."

I wondered how it must feel to look out of a window and see the bright young daisies that would shortly bloom over one's silent head. Then I looked at the little nun's quiet serene face and decided I must be the morbid one.

"You speak good French, Madame," she said presently.

I said, well, no, not really, and that I had already discovered that I understood it far, far better than I spoke it—as well I might; I'd listened to French radio programmes night after night for years.

"Oh, but I have lived in England twenty-seven years now," said the little nun, "and still I don't speak more than ten words of English. You see, we are all French. A very obstinate little corner of France, Reverend Mother always says."

And so we sat, chatting away, and the white cliffs of Dover faded behind us, and in record time, or so it seemed to me, why, we were in Calais, with French porters swarming everywhere, shouting, "Porteur! Porteur!" I beckoned to one, and he straightway grabbed both my suitcases and shot off, calling that we would meet again in the Customs. Then I helped the little nun tie the plants for Maman and Papa's grave on her leather valise with a tape-measure she found in her string bag, and we wished each other the very warmest goodbye. She said she only had to take a bus now and she would be home. Of course, there would be the Customs first, but that would not take long. I said I sincerely hoped not, and we shook hands once more, and I sped after my porter and my two suitcases.

Again I was lucky. A tired-looking Customs officer gave one look at me and my cases, rattled off a volley of questions, didn't wait for an answer, slapped a scrawl in yellow chalk on both of them, turned to another officer and groaned, "Mon Dieu! Have I a satanic toothache!"

"Toothache, eh!" grinned the other. "Well, you know what they say, my lad! Toothache means love-ache!"

"Not at my age, it doesn't," sighed the other, most regretfully I thought. "Not at my age! It means dentists, that's all." He sighed again, and I took it I was no longer required and that I might take my place in the train for Paris.

Again luck was with me. My indomitable porter found me a corner seat by unceremoniously pushing along an expensive valise, that I felt must belong to the well-dressed annoyed-looking woman opposite me, slung up my two cases, pocketed his tip with a swift, "Merci, Madame", and was off to look for other burdened travellers.

The lady opposite me pointedly buried her face in a very glossy magazine, and I sat there, looking out of the window, but seeing very little, I'm afraid, my heart singing joyously and idiotically, "France! France! This is France!" to the rhythm of the train.

For some reason or another, the train unexpectedly stopped for a few minutes at a country halt. I didn't catch the name. And down the little platform panted a short stout gentleman in a fine navy-blue uniform with plenty of gold braid on it, peaked cap on his head, but carpet slippers on his feet.

I suppose I was smiling as he padded by, for he swept off his cap, beamed back at me and asked, "You 'appy, Missus, eh?"

"Yes," I said. "Very happy, thank you."

"Then, tha's-so-kay!" he grinned, and shot off down the platform.

"Well, really!" said the well-dressed woman. "The French are an extraordinary lot, don't you think? I adore France, of course, such a lovely country, but I simply cannot stand the French!"

"Dear me!" I said. "Now I wonder if anyone thinks the same of Britain and the British."

She stared at me for a moment as if unable to believe her ears. Then I think she wrote me off as half-witted, for not another word did we exchange the rest of the way to Paris.

Paris. Now I swear I intended to spend an instructive week or so in Paris. Indeed as I made my way to the taxis waiting outside the station I had one of my suitable addresses ready in my hand. But suddenly the strangest feeling swept over me. It was as if something deep within me was tugging at me, begging me to listen, urging me to travel on. I sharply told myself that this was arrant nonsense, that I ought to see something of Paris first, that I had plenty of time.

But it was no use. I shall never explain it, but I found myself getting into a taxi, I heard myself say, "Gare de Lyon, s'il vous plaît," and away we went. And there I sat, hanging on to my seat for dear life, wondering what on earth was coming over me, wondering even more frantically if Parisian taxis did sometimes arrive safe and whole, as we charged ahead regardless, and policemen, blowing whistles and flicking white batons, and tall buildings and people all scattered before us.

At the Gare de Lyon I paid up like a lamb; I didn't even attempt to argue about the tip demanded, I was far too grateful to be standing on a beautiful safe pavement once more. Then I put my two cases in the station cloakroom and walked down a couple of back streets till I spotted a little restaurant with a blackboard outside which said in yellow chalk:

The Golden Pig offers the Best Fixed Price
Repast in Paris. Served at all hours. Come
in hungry and walk out happy.

So I went in, but before I could ask for the best fixed-price repast in Paris the proprietor came out from behind his zinc-topped bar, handed me a menu, and addressed me—in English. "All explicated in Engleesch this one. You indicate, Madame. Me, I understand okay."

The trouble was that I didn't understand his all-English menu, especially when I came to "chise". Suddenly light dawned, and up bobbed the schoolmistress in me—I never can quite keep the woman down—and I suggested it might be clearer spelt c-h-e-e-s-e as in England. The proprietor considered this for a moment. Then he shook his head. "No, no, Madame! In winter perhaps, but in summer definitely no! In summer it is not calm like now. Many Engleesch and Americans eating here. So I engage a type called Vladimir. Very good boy, this Vladimir, but from Middle-Europe. Very little French, and only Yes, No, Please, Okay in Engleesch.

Not like me. I speak dam good, eh? Now if I write c-h-e-e-s-e as you say, then what happens? I will tell you. You will indicate c-h-e-e-s-e. This Vladimir will look. 'Ah, chaise!' he cries and runs. But what will be bring you? A chair! Yes, Madame, a chair to sit on. So I think I leave 'chise', then Vladimir bawls 'Cheese!' and I give him cheese. That way, everybody 'appy!"

Very cheered by my fixed-price repast, I then strolled back to the station. On the way I bought half a dozen postcards, wrote, "In Paris. Lovely weather" on the lot and slid them in a letter-box. Then I smothered my conscience, recovered my two suitcases, and bought myself a ticket—for Nîmes, single, third-class.

Now everybody I knew who had travelled in France had kindly taken the trouble to warn me that third-class in French trains was not very comfortable. And it wasn't. But I would not have missed it for the world, apart from the fact that I knew I simply had to go easy with my money.

There was a whole family in my compartment, also travelling down to Nîmes, Papa, Maman, and five children, all girls, the youngest about four and the oldest fifteen or so. And as we were going to spend the whole night in the train, they sensibly set to work to make themselves comfortable. They began by taking off their shoes and putting on warm slippers. Then they took off their coats and Maman neatly folded them, and piled them on the rack over our heads together with their shoes, handbags, gloves and jaunty little hats. This settled, they unpacked another suitcase and they all got into warm jerseys and pullovers. Papa then unfolded the evening paper and began to read us out interesting extracts of the day's news, whilst Maman pulled out a large box of curlers and she and the girls proceeded to roll up everybody else's hair for the night. I offered to lend a hand with this, and Maman promptly handed me a fistful of curlers and said perhaps I'd be kind enough to take on Vonvon, the little four-year-old sitting by my side.

Then when everybody was all set for the night, including a little trip each down the corridor—Maman ordering them all off one after the other, Papa got down a big basket, and they spread newspapers on their laps and began to have their supper. Papa took out a very long thin loaf and cut off chunks all round. Maman handed out slices of sausage, hard-boiled eggs and pieces of cheese. And they washed all this down with red wine which Papa poured out in two glasses that they passed round and round. They kindly pressed me to have a little drink and something to eat too, but I said I'd just had a good meal so unfortunately I wasn't hungry or thirsty, but I thanked them very warmly, all the same.

Whereupon Papa said, "Ah! I hear you are English. Our Marie-Thérèse here, she learns your language. Speak to the lady in English, Marie-Thérèse!"

Marie-Thérèse, very red and anguished, said, "Good day!" and waited. I gathered it was my turn now, so I said, "Oh, good day, Marie-Thérèse!"

"Ow hare you?" returned Marie-Thérèse."

"Very well, thank you," I said. "And how are you?"

"Me, too," said Marie-Thérèse thankfully and got on with her egg.

"But continue, name of a pipe!" cried Papa outraged.

"Speak some more, will you! Is that all you can say after one year of it?"

Marie-Thérèse took a deep breath and tried again. "Me, I am French girl. I 'ave feefteen years. Ow many 'ave you, please?"

At this triumph, Papa smiled proudly at Maman, and, to Marie-Thérèse's great relief, we all slipped back into French once more.

They asked me how the Royal Family were, and I said, "Oh, splendid!" as if I'd come straight from Buckingham Palace.

Marie-Thérèse said she wished they had real princesses, too, and Papa said, well, really, that girl positively covered him with shame—they *did* have princesses in France, royal ones at that; but, of course, good republicans like them only admired the princesses of other nations. Maman then said she knew someone whose cousin had married a Meestaire Smeete of Soot-am-ton. Maybe I knew him. I worked this out to be Mr. Smith of Southampton, and I said I was sorry but I'd not had the pleasure of meeting him. Marie-Thérèse then asked about the fogs in London, and was most disappointed to hear I hadn't been lost in one yet.

Then little Vonvon fell asleep, her head against my arm. And I said no, no, they weren't to disturb her, I was quite comfortable.

Papa said, ah, talking of comfort, was it the same in England—but no, it wouldn't be, of course, the English being a sensible fair-minded race—this racket of second class he meant. Now, in France, every soul connected with the railway, every living soul, together with both their parents and all their brothers, sisters, cousins, aunts and uncles—or so it seemed to him—they all travelled free. FREE! Anywhere they liked, north, south, east, west and second class if I pleased! SECOND CLASS! Indeed I could take it from him, said Papa, that on that very train nine out of ten of those gentlemen and ladies lolling in luxury in second class were doing it free. FREE! And who paid for all these carefree travellers, these energetic globe-trotters? We did! We, the poor devils, sitting there, cooped up in third class. We paid for them. *We* did.

"I tell you," said Papa, "I tell you, Miss, this Government of ours . . ."

But Maman and the girls had obviously heard Papa's views on second-class travel and the Government before. Eyes began to shut, heads began to nod, Papa began to grow hoarse, and presently there we all were, sometimes half awake, sometimes half asleep. And the night seemed very, very long and not at all comfortable, but oh, so kind and friendly.

Suddenly Papa gave a shout that made us all jump. "Nîmes!" he cried. "We arrive! We arrive, I tell you! We are in Nîmes!"

And yes, the train was definitely slowing down; we were steaming into Nîmes.

I'll never forget it, never! Papa bundled out all the children, still half asleep, still in their slippers and curlers, whilst Maman and I pulled down the window and hurled out the coats, hats, shoes, gloves, baskets, and suitcases. And all the while Papa danced up and down on the platform shouting instructions, and stopping every now and then to yell down to the guard, daring him to do a thing till we were ready, I gathered. And the guard shouted back—certainly, certainly, let Monsieur take his time about issuing equipment to his little orphanage, he'd wait all day if necessary, of course, and to blazes with the timetables of the Railways of France. Naturally Papa wasn't going to let this pass without asserting his rights as a passenger who paid, but at last the train steamed out and there we were, Papa, Maman, all five girls and me, breathless but victorious, all our luggage to a shoe stacked about us.

Then Marie-Thérèse and I helped Maman sort out the hats, coats, gloves, handbags and shoes, and we dressed the younger ones and took out all the curlers. And then we picked up the baskets and suitcases and trooped out behind Papa, into the cold grey morning.

"Ah!" said Papa. "Now we must take a bus. We live just outside Nîmes. But first Miss must have some breakfast with us! Yes, yes, I insist!"

He led the way to a café across the road. We filed in, piled the luggage behind the door, and sat down at a long table near a comfortable stove. A sleepy waiter came out, said, "Coffee with milk for everybody? Certainly, Monsieur!" and went to get it.

In less than five minutes we all had great basin-sized cups of coffee steaming in front of us, and Maman, economical as they make them, pulled out the remains of the loaf, cut it into eight, handed us each a chunk, and we all dipped it into our coffee. And, believe me, I never enjoyed a breakfast more in all my life.

Presently I said I wondered if they had ever heard of a Café-Restaurant des Monuments de Nîmes.

"Café-Restaurant des Monuments!" roared Papa. "But of course! An old friend of mine keeps it. We were in the same regiment together. Oh, what a pair of young troopers we were!"

"It's not a big place," said Maman. "Quite small, in fact. But very clean."

"And the cooking!" exclaimed Papa and kissed the tips of his fingers. "All butter! None of this margarine. Look, Miss, you say you have met us. I'll give you our address."

He searched in his pockets and found an old envelope. "There," he said, and handed it to me. "That's us. Jules Tardy, Negotiator in Wines, Saint Didier of the Vines, only ten kilometres from Nîmes. You'll be staying some time, no? You will want to see the Roman Monuments, of course. But if you have a free moment, why not come out to see us one day?"

"Yes," said Maman eagerly, "do come. Saint Didier isn't much of a place, vineyards everywhere, but very quiet and pretty."

"Yes, yes, do come! You must come, Miss," chorused all the girls, and I said I'd be delighted. And I meant it.

At this moment Papa looked up at the clock. "The bus!" he cried. "To the bus! And at the gallop, too, if you please!"

We gulped down the rest of our coffee, grabbed the luggage and tore out, Papa paying the waiter as he ran. As we turned the corner, there stood the bus, about to start.

The driver, grumbling most eloquently, climbed down from his high seat and swarmed up a little ladder to inspect the roof already piled with suitcases, baskets, three bicycles, a wicker-work pram, a large tin bath, and an enormous wreath of purple china flowers with a white china dove perched on it.

"Ah no!" stormed the driver. Devil take him, not another article could he squeeze in. But Papa, deaf as a post, blandly went on handing up the luggage, which the driver, still protesting, then contrived to ram in between the bath and the pram.

This settled, Maman and all the girls shook hands with me and climbed into the bus. Then Papa shook hands with me, and he got in. And the driver, tearing his hair, inquired, "Alors . . . tout le monde y est?", expressed his real sentiments with a blast of the klaxon, and off they rattled, all the Tardys leaning out of the windows, waving, and calling, "Au revoir, Miss! Au revoir! Et merci!"

I waved till they were out of sight, then I put the envelope safely away in my bag, picked up my two cases, and crossed the road again to the taxis waiting outside the station. I got into one, and said, "Café-Restaurant des Monuments de Nîmes, s'il vous plaît."

"Café-Restaurant des Monuments de Nîmes?" echoed the driver, and the look on his face plainly added, "Never heard of it!"

He leaned out and yelled to another taxi. "Dis-donc, Numa, le Café-Restaurant des Monuments?"

He and Numa then went at it hammer and tongs, but presently Numa must have convinced my driver there was such a place, for he slipped in his clutch and off we went.

And I sat there, clutching my handbag, my heart suddenly beating like a sledge-hammer.

"Well, this is it!" I said to myself. "Nîmes, where your father lived! Now what do you propose to do? Yes, what *are* you going to do?" And for the first time since I left home I began to feel scared, scared at the way I'd flung up everything, come all this way, spent all this money. . . .

"Admit it!" I told myself. "You're half-hoping you'll come across somebody related to you, somebody who will welcome you with open arms."

And very likely that was. My father left Nîmes over fifty years ago. Fifty years. Not to mention two World Wars and the way they uprooted people. Better look facts in the face. It would be nothing short of a miracle if I came across anyone who even remembered my father and his family. Better fix my mind on seeing as much of France as my money would allow.

And I saw myself, guide-book in hand, wandering endlessly round the sights, alone, till my money gave out.

6

The Monuments of Nîmes

Suddenly I realised that the driver was talking to me, grumbling away at the names of the streets, I gathered.

"Now perhaps you can tell me, Madame," he was asking; "this Peek-a-dee-lee of yours, over there in London, is it still called Peek-a-dee-lee?"

"Why, yes," I said. "At least it was when I left home."

"Ah!" said the driver, very satisfied. "That's precisely what I tell them. Taxi-drivers over there have the devil's own luck. Now if it was over here in France, that Peek-a-dee-lee of yours, it would have changed its name at least a dozen times. Listen, Madame. I am not Methuselah as you can see, but I know one avenue that in my time alone has been Avenue Czar Nicolas, Avenue Lord Kitchener, Avenue King of the Belgians, Avenue President Roosevelt, Avenue Maréchal Pétain, and now—but only for the time being, of course—it is Avenue Lake Success! I ask you! I ask you!"

He gave a passionate blast on his klaxon, swerved at top speed round a corner, shouted back indignantly at two flying pedestrians and snorted, "And to complicate further one's existence, types like that think the middle of a road is the very place for a nice quiet stroll.

"But it should be somewhere about here," he went on, "this café-restaurant of yours. And you see how it is— cafés to the right, cafés to the left, and as like as not all changing their names twice weekly. Café Saint Baudile on Monday, Café Comrade Karl Marx on Friday. It's a mania, I tell you, Madame, a positive mania!"

He turned into a quiet square shaded with plane trees, and my heart gave a sudden lurch. There, in the far corner, I thought I saw it.

"This will do, thank you," I said hurriedly. "Put me down here, please."

"As you please," said the driver, plainly thinking I must be something of a maniac, too. He drew up, and I got out, paid him, picked up my two suitcases, and made for the other end of the square. I sat down on a bench under one of the trees. I had to, my legs felt so queer.

There, across the road, right opposite me, there it was —the Café-Restaurant des Monuments de Nîmes, exactly as in my old photograph. I couldn't believe it, but there it was. There it was.

And more unbelievable still, over the door, and freshly painted, too, it still said: Marius Durand. Café-Restaurant des Monuments de Nîmes. Chambres pour Voyageurs.

But now there were two extra words: Confort Moderne. Modern Comfort.

As I looked and looked, out through the door ran a little boy in a neat black overall, flew across the road and nearly fell over my suitcases.

"Zut!" he said, and then, catching sight of me, "Oh, pardon, Madame!"

For a moment he stared at me with round dark eyes. Then he pulled a ball from his pocket. "You watch this, Madame," he said, and began to bounce it higher and higher.

"Pierre!" called an exasperated voice, and there in the doorway of the Café-Restaurant des Monuments de Nîmes stood a stout middle-aged gentleman in a white shirt, striped trousers, blue apron about his waist, and black slippers on his feet.

"Ah non!" he cried, and rushed across the road, grabbed the ball with one hand, and shook the little boy with the other. "Tell me," he exploded. "Just tell me how many times I am to explain that it is dangerous to play with that ball over here? The ball flies in the road. You fly to get it. And one day where will you fly? I will tell you. Right under the wheels of a motor car!"

"Or an American jeep," put in the small boy.

"Or an American jeep," agreed the gentleman. "And there you will be, rolled flat okay, as flat as an American pancake, flatter in fact. Won't he, Madame?"

"Well," I said, "it certainly won't improve him."

The gentleman looked at me. "Ah, Madame herself is from America perhaps?"

"No," I said, "England. And I was wondering if I could book a room for a while. . . ."

And I waved towards the Café-Restaurant des Monuments de Nîmes as if I thought that might suit me as well as any other place.

"But certainly, Madame," said the gentleman. "Certainly! Permit me." He stuffed the ball into the pocket of his apron, seized my two suitcases and started off. So

I seized the small boy, and, hand in hand, we followed him across the road.

Any minute now, I told myself, and I'd wake up.

But this time it was no dream. I was there, really there, inside the Café-Restaurant des Monuments de Nîmes.

I was standing in a long narrow room. A row of little tables ran down either side; at the far end was a high wooden counter, and behind this counter, against the wall, rose shelf upon shelf of brightly coloured bottles.

And there was something about this room, something warm and welcoming, something very gay yet orderly— the cherry-red chairs, the red and blue checked table-cloths, the shining brass bands about the wooden counter. And, standing on it, a great bunch of deep red carnations stuffed tightly into a tall glass jug.

The gentleman must have noticed me looking at them, for he said—in English this time, "Ah! You like these flowers, no? Me, too. They cost the eyes from my head, but still I buy some. Oh yes, I speak some English; like a Spanish cow, eh? But I speak it just the same but only when I have the opportunity, of course. Angélique! Angélique!"

Out through a door to one side of the counter came a short stocky young woman, her dark hair most beautifully rolled in curls on the top of her head.

"Take Madame up to room seven," said the gentleman and handed her a key from a board on the wall.

"By the way," I said, "are you the proprietor?"

"Yes," he said, "since four years, Madame."

"Then I met friends of yours on the train," I told him.

88

"A family called Tardy. They asked me to give you their very warmest regards."

He threw up delighted hands. "So you have met this good old Jules and his troupe of girls, eh? Beautiful family, no?"

"Yes," I said. "Lovely."

"Oh, but we must certainly have a little talk about them," he beamed; "but please forgive me if I now fly back to the kitchen. I keep both eyes on all the cooking. But please demand Angélique here if you want something."

"Thank you," I said. "I will."

I followed Angélique up a flight of steep stairs, no carpet, but very well scrubbed, and along a narrow landing.

"Voilà!" said Angélique and unlocked and threw open the door of a very dark room. Then she rushed to the windows and flung open the tall shutters. And in danced the sunshine and lit up room seven.

"Pretty, isn't it?" said Angélique. "And clean! Take a look, Madame!"

She pulled back the yellow quilt and patted the sheets and a long, sausage-shaped bolster. And they were indeed clean, as white as snow.

"You like pillows as well perhaps?" asked Angélique. "In here!"

She opened the wardrobe door, and there on the top shelf were two enormous square pillows.

"And here," said Angélique, waving to a very small basin fitted with two outsize taps, "running water, cold and hot, very hot, the hot, especially at night."

"Splendid!" I said. "Nothing like modern comfort, is there?"

"Oh, but that's not all," said Angélique. "There is also the Vah-taire. I'll show you, Madame. This way!"

She led the way along the landing and flung open another door. And there, well, there was what we politely call the toilet.

"Very modern," said Angélique and pulled the flush to prove it. "As for comfort, why, that seat alone cost the sky. Real mahogany, none of this clever imitation. I saw the bill with my own two eyes."

As she proudly closed the door on this last word in modern comfort, she pointed to W.C. painted in large gold letters on the door.

"English, eh?" said Angélique. "Vah-taire Cloosette, no? But we haven't the time for all that. We just say the Vah-taire.

"You will be staying a few days of course," went on Angélique, following me back to my room, and obviously dying to get on with the conversation. "Nîmes isn't a bad place, though I come from Nice myself. And there are Roman monuments here, you know. But, of course, you know. That is probably why you have come to Nîmes—to look at the monuments. The Americans and English all adore looking at them."

She paused and looked at me expectantly. So I said I was sure I'd adore looking at them too.

"I thought so," said Angélique very satisfied. "And this is quite a good little hotel, you'll find. Not like some we have in Nice, of course, where the rich Americans go. But the food here is good. And clean! I'll say it's clean! Between ourselves Monsieur is something of a crank about all this hygiene. But there, men are always peculiar about something or the other, aren't they, Madame?"

I began to say I wouldn't know, but Angélique rattled straight on, "I've been working here for four years now. I'm very fond of little Pierre, not that he can't be a proper little camel at times. Will dawdle so, especially on my night out. And my fiancé comes from Marseilles and you know what they are. Hopping-mad if a girl turns up ten minutes late. And jealous! Suspicious! Mind you, that's how it should be, of course. No girl likes to be taken for granted. But the way he carries on, well, it gets a little wearing at times. But there, that's life, that is. All or nothing. No moderation.

"Ah well, I suppose I'd better be going. We start serving at twelve."

She paused in the doorway. "You try the 'brandade', Madame. It's really very good here. Oh, and please shout down the stairs if you want me again."

I thanked her and said I would; and as the door closed behind her I sat down on the bed and, well, took in room seven.

The wallpaper, for instance. I'd never seen anything like it. Sunflower yellow with wide green satin stripes running from ceiling to floor, and trailing in and out of these stripes, long sprays of lilac, every flower twice as large as life and twice as purple.

On the foot of the bed over the yellow quilt, a square crimson eiderdown, not quilted, but all in one billowy piece like an outsize cushion.

On the highly polished green linoleum, three green rugs patterned all over with pink roses.

And the tall windows, all four of them, were shrouded in long cream curtains, lace ones. Mrs. Penny would have loved them, I thought. She dearly liked a bold, handsome pattern.

Oh, I know it sounds terrible. But, oddly enough, it wasn't. At least not to me. To my mind there was something warm and jolly about room seven. It reminded me of Mrs. Penny's parlour. She liked plenty of cheerful colour, too, bless her.

Yes, I liked room seven.

Then I went to the windows, opened them wide, and looked out on the square across the road. Children were playing and shouting under the plane trees, the very trees under which my father must have played, with Mariette-Louise, and Alexandrine.

And I leaned on the windowsill, thinking of all that world of make-believe I had once invented about this very place and finding it hard to believe that I was there, really there, till the sensible side of me began nagging. "Well? What about a wash? What about unpacking?"

So I turned to and unpacked my suitcases, and washed as best as I could in the tiny basin. And, to my surprise, when I went downstairs it was half-past twelve, and the long narrow dining-room was packed with gentlemen, serviettes tucked into their waistcoats, enjoying their food and talking sixteen to the dozen.

And there was the proprietor in a spotless white coat now, but still in his slippers, dancing here, there and everywhere, talking and laughing with everyone in turn, but keeping an eagle eye on Angélique and another bustling waitress, I noticed.

"Ah!" he cried as he spotted me. "I have a very nice place reserved for you!" He waved me into a chair opposite a pleasant-looking woman about my own age, and handed me a large, closely written menu. "I leave you a moment to decide, Madame," he said and shot off to shake hands with a portly gentleman just about to leave.

I suppose I must have looked as bewildered as I felt as I studied all the dishes I could order if I felt so inclined, for the woman opposite me said, "The fixed price lunch is quite good today, Madame."

"Oh, thank you," I said. "That'll save me a lot of bother." Then I remembered Angélique's advice. "By the way," I said, "what *is* a 'brandade'?"

She said it was a speciality of Nîmes, but one had to make it properly, of course. One just *had* to stand over a 'brandade' stirring all the time, adding all the olive oil, drop by drop, till everything was rich and creamy. Then one had to know the precise amounts of chopped truffles and salt, and last, but not least, one had to be generous but not exaggerated with the pepper.

I said it sounded wonderful, but I'd been travelling all night, so I thought I'd better try something not quite so rich and creamy. A little fish perhaps.

And she said the 'brandade' *was* fish, boiled cod-fish to be exact, but their way of cooking it here in Nîmes translated it into a real miracle. But, of course, not everybody's liver could stand up to miracles, especially after a long journey, and, in my place, she would settle on a little plain "bifteck".

So I settled on a little plain "bifteck", and when it arrived it was the biggest beefsteak I'd seen in years, cooked in butter, sprinkled all over with chopped parsley, and festooned with a high bank of watercress and fried potatoes. And by its side was a great bowl of crisp salad.

All this, of course, had broken the ice very nicely, and my new friend was now telling me that she was a widow and worked in the post office, but that she didn't relish a solitary life and cooking for herself alone, so she boarded here in the Café-Restaurant des Monuments de Nîmes, but spent her three weeks' holiday-with-pay with her married daughter, Estelle, in Toulouse.

And I told her that I wasn't married, that I was in France for a long holiday, and that I lived in England.

She said, well, she'd guessed as much from the cut of my coat, and that my French was rather too correct if I didn't mind her saying so.

I said of course I didn't, and that I'd really have to see what I could do about it.

Then she told me that these gentleman I could see doing themselves so proud were businessmen. They only came in to lunch, often with clients they wished to soften up, if I knew what she meant. Funny, wasn't it, the way good food and good wine could mellow the toughest masculine heart? But for dinner now, these gentlemen went home to their wives. At least one hoped they did. So in the evening it wasn't like this at all; it was very quiet, in fact; just a few regulars, as one might say. Indeed, that's what they called themselves "the regulars". I'd be meeting them all tonight, of course.

She then said she supposed I had come to Nîmes to see the Roman monuments, of course; and that if I liked she would come so far with me and set me on the right road for the Temple of Diana.

So we drank up our coffee, folded our enormous ser-viettes—I noticed she slipped hers into a neat linen envelope—and as we started for the door, the proprietor waved and called, "Ah! You go to see the Roman monuments, yes? Well, make a good promenade. Till tonight then, Madame!"

Five minutes later I shook hands with the friendly widow, and she went off to her post office and I set course, as directed, down a wide avenue—on my way to the Roman monuments, since everybody seemed so very determined about it.

But it was a lovely day. The sun shone in a warm blue sky, a little wind danced in the trees, and all down the long avenue the cafés—and there seemed to be dozens of them—had set little tables and chairs outside on the pavements. Everywhere I looked other people seemed to be sitting about, sensibly taking it easy, enjoying the spring sunshine. So presently I sat down, too, at one of these little tables, and ordered a pot of tea.

And out it came with a little label dangling from the lid: So-and-so's Tea. One Dose.

I was about to pour it straight out when the waiter froze in his tracks and threw up both hands in genuine dismay. "But be reasonable, Madame!" he implored. "Give it a chance! Let it infuse, Madame!"

When his back was turned, I lifted the lid, and there was the dose for one, tied up in a neat little muslin bag floating in warm water. So I decided I had better let it infuse. And I sat there, watching the people stroll by: small girls, dainty as dolls, swinging little handbags; wiry imps of boys in very short shorts and very long socks; old people touchingly neat in decent black.

I was just pouring out my infusion when a gendarme crossed the road, closely handcuffed to an unshaven gentleman in a curious shaggy fur coat. "Ho—oh! Business good, oh?" called a voice behind me. The gendarme turned, spotted some friends, and threaded his way through the tables to shake hands with them all, the gentleman in the fur coat standing politely by, of course, then there was another round of hand-shaking, and off they went once more.

"Ah!" said the lady in deep mourning sitting at the table next to mine. "Something tells me that rascal probably pinched that nice coat. What do you think, Madame? Oh, what a world we live in, don't we, Madame?"

I said we most certainly did. And she said, then what about the price of everything. Scandalous, wasn't it? This new mourning of hers, for instance, now that had cost a pretty packet, she could tell me. But there, one could but try to do one's duty.

She sighed so hard, that I hastily said yes, one could but try. And she dived into her enormous handbag and pulled out a mourning-card, the size of a postcard, with a wide black frilly edge, and handed it to me.

"I had three dozen of them printed," she said. "The very best quality. The picture's on the other side."

So I turned the card over, and there was the photograph of an old lady, looking extremely sour.

"My aunt," she explained. "And a bad-tempered old skinflint if ever there was one. She didn't like me any more than I liked her, but I was her only relative and she did her duty by me. Left me her house and all the furniture, so I'm doing my duty by her."

I looked at the wide black crêpe armband on her heavy black coat, the black crêpe bow on her black hat, the crêpe hem on the long black veil hanging down her back, the black shoes and stockings, and I said, yes, I could see she was.

At this moment a pair of young lovers came sauntering by, and perhaps it was the sight of all that deep mourning that made them think of their own bright happiness, for they suddenly stopped, flung their arms about each other and kissed most passionately. And sauntered on, caught up in a shining world all their own.

"Ah! Love!" sighed the lady in black. "Wonderful, isn't it?"

I said cautiously that I supposed it must be. She looked at me, very surprised. "Now, don't tell me," she said, "that you haven't had an affair or two in your time. Your figure's still quite nice, you know."

I smiled, and tried to look like a woman with a romantic affair or so behind her, thought better of it, and poured out the rest of my infusion instead.

Then a gentleman in a gaudy tartan jacket with a fur collar came down the avenue selling picture-postcards. And he gave one look at me, sitting there, drinking tea, and hared across.

97

"Good day, Missus. Very nice postcards, Missus? All the Roman monuments! You look, Missus. Please look, Missus!"

Having looked at the Roman monuments, I felt obliged to buy a few, of course. Then I ordered another pot of tea and said I'd like boiling water with this dose, please. The waiter said, "Certainly, Madame!" and came back with it, together with a small jug of boiling milk, and a writing-pad fitted with blotting paper.

"There," he said. "Now you can write your cards in comfort, Madame."

So I wrote my cards in comfort out there in the warm sunshine.

"In Nîmes. Lovely weather. Wonderful Roman monuments."

The lady in mourning then told me that I could buy stamps just down the avenue at the tobacconist's, so presently I got up and went to the tobacconist's, bought the stamps, stuck them on, found a letter-box and posted the lot.

Then I stood for a moment and looked down the avenue. It looked very, very long; longer than ever.

"Well, what's the hurry?" I asked myself. "The Roman monuments have been there these two thousand years. They'll wait another day."

And I went back to my little table and sat down. Out danced the waiter, very delighted to see me again.

"Tea, no, Madame?"

"Tea, yes," I agreed. "With boiling water but cold milk, please. I prefer it that way."

And there I sat, blissfully doing nothing, not even

thinking, going one better than the poet. He *stood* and stared. I sat.

Presently it grew dusk and a little chilly; and when I looked at my watch I was staggered to see it was nearly six o'clock. So I got to my feet and started back for the Café-Restaurant des Monuments de Nîmes.

I hadn't seen a single monument, but I didn't care. No, I didn't care.

And behind me came the voice of the waiter. "Au revoir, Madame! And thank you, thank you!"

And the warmth in his voice assured me that it wasn't only the modest tip I had left him. No, no, he now definitely regarded me as a valued customer, almost a friend.

7

Monsieur Tallon Receives a Letter

When I walked in, there was only little Pierre in the dining-room, serviette tied round his neck, glowering at a plateful of soup.

"Me!" he said. "Me, I always have to go to bed early. Every night I have to swallow down my soup and then, psst! Straight up to bed!"

"Splendid!" I said. "Then you will grow up a big strong boy."

But Pierre had heard this line of talk before. "I know," he said, politely exasperated, "I know. But I'd much rather go to bed late *now*. Much rather."

"Listen," I said. "When you've finished your supper, you knock at my door, and I'll show you something from England."

"Ah! Chic alors!" said Pierre and got down to his soup.

In less than ten minutes he was knocking at my door. I invited him in, and he sat down on my bed whilst I unpacked the little china house that I had left wrapped up in my suitcase. I set it on the high chest of drawers, and then I found my torch and fixed it behind—just as Mrs. Penny used to fix an end of candle for me. And I switched it on.

The little house shone out in the shadowy room, and Pierre breathed, "Chic! Oh, chic!" and sat staring at it, very still and silent.

"Listen," he said presently. "Now make the smoke come out of the chimneys!"

A loud knock at the door saved the situation.

"Don't open it!" hissed Pierre. "Don't take any notice. It's only Angélique wanting to put me to bed."

He was right. It was Angélique, and she did want to put him to bed, and at the gallop, too, and no back answers, if he pleased. It was her night out and she still had her blouse to iron and, as she'd told me, her Placide got absolutely savage if she turned up late.

So Pierre politely shook hands with me and went off, dragging his feet and saying, "All right! All right! I *am* hurrying. Can't you see I'm hurrying!" And I went downstairs to see about a meal.

There were now four gentlemen in the dining-room having a quiet drink with the proprietor. As soon as he saw me, he opened a big ledger on the table in front of him, held out a pen, and said, "Ah! I must ask you to sign the book, please! The police demand it, not me, Madame!"

So I signed the book: Dorothy F. Durand.

"Durand!" he cried. "Ah no! Don't tell me you have Durands over in England, too!"

"Well, no," I said. "As a matter of fact, my father was French. His name was Marius Durand."

"Marius Durand! But that's my name, too! Not that there's anything remarkable about that. Thousands of us called Marius. Hundreds of thousands of us called

Durand, so Marius Durand, why, it's like John Smith in England, eh?"

"Well, no," I said. "In this case it really is extraordinary. You see, my grandfather was also called Marius Durand and he lived *here*, in this very house. And so did my father before he went to England. If you'll wait a moment, I'll show you a photograph I've brought with me."

I ran upstairs and came down with the photograph of the Café-Restaurant des Monuments de Nîmes, and my grandfather sitting at a little table on the pavement outside.

"Look," I said. "My grandfather. And that's his name over the door, that very door, Marius Durand, just as it is now!"

"Ah! Ça par exemple!" cried Monsieur Durand, and sank down in a chair.

Then everyone burst into speech at once. I gathered that Monsieur Durand had bought the business from a Madame Widow Legrand, and she had bought it from a Monsieur Emile Dupont, and he had bought it from a Monsieur Rigaud, but nobody could remember much about that gentleman or who came before him. People came; people went; especially during the last war.

"All the same," said Monsieur Durand, and rose to his feet, "permit me, another Marius Durand, to be the first to welcome you to the home of your grandpapa."

And he shook hands with me in the friendliest way. So did all the other gentlemen. Then they insisted I took a little glass of something to celebrate the occasion, something they called "pastis" but which tasted remarkably like aniseed balls to me.

Then the pleasant-looking woman with whom I'd had lunch came in, and, of course, she had to hear the story and examine the photograph. And we had another round of "pastis" so she could welcome me to my grandpapa's home, too. And as she sipped it, she happened to turn over the photograph.

"Listen to this!" she chuckled.

> "*Artistic Photography in all Branches.*
> *Popular and Parisian.*
> *Numerous Gold Medals and other High Awards.*
> *Installation of Electricity permits Operation at Night*
> *Children a Speciality.*
> *August Tallon,*
> *4, Place de la Glacière,*
> *Nîmes.*"

"Tallon! Place de la Glacière!" cried one of the gentlemen. "But there's a photographer called Tallon still living there! Just a moment! Excuse me!"

He grabbed his hat and made for the door. In less than ten minutes he was back with another breathless gentleman in his shirt-sleeves and no collar.

"Here is Monsieur Tallon himself!" he said triumphantly. "He was only too glad to come along when I explained matters."

Monsieur Tallon shook hands all round and then examined the photograph.

"But certainly!" he said. "My grandfather must

definitely have taken this. Bit of an exaggeration about all those gold medals, though! We only found one when he died and that was the silver one he won in a pigeon-shooting competition. But he was always hoping to win a few, of course. Very optimistic old gentleman, my grandpapa. Oh yes, he's been dead these twenty years, but my grandmama is still alive. Ninety-three next birthday and nearly blind, but there's nothing wrong with her hearing, or her memory. So I'll tell you what I'll do. I'll write and find out if she remembers what happened to your family. If anyone can tell you, my grandmama will. She was interested in everybody's business. Still is, in fact. That's why she's lived so long. Far too busy to die. But I warn you it may take some time to get an answer. You see, she's living with my Aunt Pélagie now. And my Aunt Pélagie is one of these ladies who do everything to a time-table. She writes all her letters on the first Sunday of every month. It's her Sunday for writing, and she wouldn't sit down and reply on any other day, no, not if the President himself was burning to hear from her. But don't worry, she'll write then and tell me every word my grandmama has to say about your family. She's a most conscientious woman, my Aunt Pélagie."

I began to thank him, but he said he was only too happy, and, no, no, he wouldn't stop and have something, he had been in the middle of his dinner when Monsieur here had called, and he had better hurry back before his chop froze on his plate and his wife exploded with curiosity.

And with that, Monsieur Tallon shook hands all round once more and hurried back to his wife and his chop.

"Well!" I said. "This *is* kind of your friend!" And they said, yes, wasn't it, especially as not one of them had ever set eyes on him before.

Then they pushed two tables together and Monsieur Durand said perhaps I would like to sit down and have dinner with them. "You saw how it was at lunch," he said. "Then I trot-trot-trot. But in the evening, especially at this time of the year, it is very calm. We are always the same six or seven, never any more. So we know each other. We talk; we discuss; we sometimes play a game of 'belotte' and get very angry. Yes, we are amusing ourselves much more than if we sit, each at a little table, very silent and solitary. But permit me, Miss, to introduce you.

"You have already met Madame Muraton of the post office, of course.

"This is Monsieur Labise from the bank. He dabbles in millions all day.

"Monsieur Olivon, who has torn out all his hair teaching in the college for boys.

"Monsieur Espérandier, from those twin-brigands—the gas and electricity of France.

"And Monsieur Pinatel, who is a high-life tailor for gentlemen, *my* tailor, but he detests me to mention it."

"Well, look at him, Miss!" cried Monsieur Pinatel. "Look at him! Is he an advertisement for a tailor? Everything for comfort, and to blazes with elegance!"

"Now you know us all," beamed Monsieur Durand. "The regulars of the Café-Restaurant des Monuments de Nîmes! Will you join us?"

I said I'd like nothing better; and we all sat down to

dinner. It may have been the innocent-looking "pastis", of course; it may have been all the excitement, or the very good dinner; but now there was something very warm and festive in the air, something that made us all feel very friendly, even a little sentimental. I found myself telling them all I knew about my father's family. I brought down my album and showed them all my photographs. And they pulled photographs from their wallets and told me about their families. Then Madame Muraton went up-stairs and brought down a large photograph of her late husband, in colour; and I said he looked very dashing. And she said she'd say he was dashing! She'd always had the devil's own job holding him back from dashing after every pretty pair of legs he met, especially when he was young and lively. And those poets could sing what they liked about "where are my golden twenty years, and the snows of yesteryear" and all the romantic rest, but *she* wouldn't be young and jealous again, no, not for all the coffee in Brazil.

Then she poured out more coffee all round and said something told her, here, deep inside her, that I was definitely going to meet my family whilst I was in France.

But Monsieur Durand said, better be realists; fifty years were not precisely a week-end; and that even if I didn't come across a single loving relation, he felt that I would, nevertheless, make some very good friends.

"And," said Monsieur Pinatel, now very mellow indeed, "pray do not forget our monuments, our beautiful Roman monuments! I tell you, Miss, those Romans were like me, true artists! They cut their stone as I cut fine cloth, with deep love and respect. Let us drink a little glass to the Romans, my friends!"

So we drank a little glass to the Romans; and Monsieur Espérandier put down his glass and said, "Then there is also our sunshine, Miss! Our beautiful sunshine that bakes all our monuments a golden brown, and makes all our tenors sing like angels! Ah, Miss, you should hear Monsieur Olivon here! When I listen to him I completely forget the gas and electricity blazing away all over France. You simply must persuade him to sing for you one of these days!"

"With pleasure," said Monsieur Olivon and promptly rose to his feet and burst into song. "Eet's a long way to Tee-pah-ra-ree," he carolled, and, to my amazement, they all joined in.

Then, by special request, he obliged with a gay ballad about a bewitching little Parisienne called Mimi, a prudent young woman with her head screwed on the right way, for

> *When night did fall, when day did flee,*
> *Straight home to Mama ran little Mimi.*

In the last verse, Mimi's maidenly circumspection paid the most handsome dividends, I was pleased to hear, with Henri, the richest and best-looking of all her ardent admirers, down on his knees, imploring her to marry him, so that the chorus might run:

> *Now straight home to Henri runs little Mimi.*

After this, also by special request, I taught them all the words of the first verse of God Save the King, and we solemnly drank to the Entente Cordiale. Then Madame Muraton glanced up at the clock and cried, péchère, it was unbelievable, but it was gone midnight! So we reluctantly got to our feet, shook hands all round all over again, and said good night.

As I was going upstairs, Monsieur Durand called to me. "Miss," he said, "one moment."

He pulled a wallet from a pocket and carefully took out the photograph of a very handsome woman.

"My wife," he said quietly, in English. "She is dead when Pierre is born."

He didn't say another word, but I felt strangely moved. I knew he was paying me the very greatest compliment, that he did not show this photograph to everyone. But for the life of me, I could not find the right words to say. I looked at it for a moment and then handed it back.

"Thank you," I said. "Thank you."

"Pierre is perhaps a little like her?"

"Very like her," I assured him. "He's a grand little fellow!"

His face lit up. "You think so, too? You also think he is a very special little Durand, eh?"

We both laughed. And with that, I went on, up the stairs, to room seven.

I once read somewhere that "Happiness is a simple matter of closing the eyes", and I remember then thinking that this was not as simple as it sounded. Yet that is precisely what I did in the days that followed. I gratefully closed my eyes to everything save the warm homely little world of the Café-Restaurant des Monuments de

Nîmes where Monsieur Durand, the "regulars" and Angélique were all most kind and friendly, especially perhaps Monsieur Durand. It was almost as if he considered it his duty, his solemn duty to make me feel truly at home.

I came in one day, for instance, and found him deep in a newspaper article with a title that ran:

Oh, these English!
But let us, nevertheless, try to understand them!

"Miss," he said reproachfully, "why have you not demanded your 'five o'clocks'?"

"My 'five o'clocks'?" I asked.

"Yes," said Monsieur Durand. "I read here that it is not only a national institution, but that there is something altogether profound and symbolic about it."

"Good gracious!" I said. "Is that what it says?"

"Yes," went on Monsieur Durand. "It also says that it makes one have hope for a cooler and better world when one beholds Members of Parliament sitting on a terrace on the banks of the Thames, resolutely refusing to hurry, letting the rest of the world kick its heels, as they contemplate the pots of tea, and the plates of little cakes made, also symbolically, in the shape of little rocks."

"Miss," said Monsieur, as sober as a judge, "I cannot allow you to do without your 'five o'clock'! Ask for it at any time of the day you please!"

The weather, too, was kind and friendly. The sun shone in the bluest of skies. And I visited all the Roman monuments.

Now I'm not the one to describe them. I am no poet, no historian. But as I looked at them, I began to understand why everyone thought I must have travelled all the way to Nîmes to do just that.

There is, for instance, an exquisite little temple standing there, just as it stood in the days of the Emperor Augustus, very elegant, very poised, keeping itself to itself—and right on a wide modern avenue with cars and buses hooting past.

Then there is the Arena—a great open-air theatre, a lovely oval building with two storeys of archways all about it, and walls one hundred feet thick. Inside, on the stone seats, rising tier on tier, the Gauls and Romans once sat side by side, yelling encouragement and abuse at the gladiators fighting for their lives to make a Roman holiday.

And I was told that the apparatus is still there, and in excellent working order, with which the Romans used to flood the floor of the Arena, turning it into an oval sea complete with waves. On this, just by way of a change, fleets of little ships fought sham naval battles, though there was nothing sham about the blood that flowed, or the way the sailors frequently drowned in that cruel and churning sea.

Nowadays the people come in from miles around to yell encouragement and abuse at picadors, toreadors and matadors, and fierce, exasperated bulls.

I never went to see one of these bull-fights. The posters were enough for me, though all the "regulars" at the Café-Restaurant des Monuments de Nîmes tried hard to convince me that these bulls were a race apart, noble beasts, born fighters, who asked for no finer honour than to fight like a Christian in a Roman arena.

"Miss, they just live for that alone!" swore Monsieur Labise. "It is all they dream of, as they stare out to sea down there on those salty plains of Camargue."

"Definitely," applauded Monsieur Espérandier. "Why, it would be an insult, a deadly insult to compare the fighting bull of Provence to any of these 'ros-bif' clods!"

"Moreover," put in Monsieur Durand, "they are most intelligent. They often give as good as they get, sometimes better. I once saw a picador fly for his life, the seat of his beautiful trousers flapping like a sail in the wind. Laugh! I positively wept!"

I said I was glad to hear it. But even the possibility of pleasing reprisals like this was not enough to induce me to go.

Then I spent one long sunny day in a beautiful park set on the slopes of a hill and called the Garden of the Fountain. I took Pierre with me that day. Together we admired the marble statues, the great marble vases set about cool lakes fed by a spring that the Romans had neatly harnessed, before they set about building the Temple of Diana that stands close by—at least that is what an elderly gentleman in a straw hat told me as he, too, paused to admire the view.

Then we followed this gentleman up and up a stony winding path to the Tour Magne, a curious eight-sided tower built high on the hill. "To commemorate one of those Roman victories or the other," declared the gentleman; and he spread his handkerchief on the short, springy grass and sat down to smoke a cigarette and regain his breath.

But all this climbing had given Pierre an appetite, so we wished him good morning, and set off down the hill again, and had our lunch in the little restaurant behind the Temple of Diana. As he polished his plate with a piece of bread, Pierre said, "You don't really want to see any more, do you?"

I said, no, I thought perhaps I'd seen enough for one day.

"Chic alors!" cried young Pierre. "Now let's enjoy ourselves properly. You sit there and watch me." And he pulled out his beloved ball. So I obediently sat there in the shade of a great tree and watched him bounce and catch. And the air was very soft and warm, and full of perfume—the almond trees were in full bloom nearby. Overhead the birds chirped and sang, and, well, I could have burst into song, too. But I ordered some tea instead and a sticky drink called grenadine for Pierre; and a gardener in pale blue corduroy trousers working on a bed of pink carnations behind me said, "Ah! Makes one thirsty, all this sunshine, Madame!"

I said it certainly did, and he said, "Madame is English, no? Bit different, this, from all those fogs of yours over there."

"Now, now," I said. "We get some lovely weather, too, from time to time."

He grinned and said, well, he had a friend called Bertier, César Bertier to be exact. And this César Bertier had been in the Free French Navy all through this last war, Submarine Service. And he had once spent the whole month of February up there in Scotland, where the men wear skirts, in a town called Glass-go. And every day it rained and sleeted and blew a thousand pneumonias. In fact poor old César had even been too blue and numb to chase the girls. That would tell me how chilly it was! And César always swore he was damn glad to get back on his nice warm submarine again and get on with the war. Yes, that's what César said.

With that the gardener gave me another broad smile, and settled down to his carnations again.

We went home by bus that evening, Pierre paying our fares to the conductor who sat to one side of the door behind a little counter past which we all had to file before taking our seats. Pierre chose the two most interesting seats, of course, where he could hang his head out of a window, but as close as possible to the conductor, so we wouldn't miss a word when somebody offered a thousand-franc note for a ten-franc fare and the conductor feverishly sought for change and the help of high heaven to keep his patience.

Nor was this the end of that perfect day. As we stepped down from the bus we caught the distant poum-poum of a drum.

"Music!" screamed Pierre, and caught my hand. "Come on! Oh, come on!"

Dancing with excitement, he led the way across a great square, and there, standing before the bandstand, were four most elegant young men in pale grey suits, shining brass buttons, wide flowing ties of rose-coloured satin, and yellow suède shoes. As we came near, with drum, saxophone, trumpet and clarionet, they burst into melody.

I couldn't believe my ears. It was a hymn, a most familiar hymn: "Count your Blessings."

Then they slung down their instruments, put their heads together, and sang it in harmony, close American harmony. And somebody pushed a leaflet in my hand which informed me that I was listening to the famous Musical Male Quartet, all the way from Hollywood, who could play sixteen instruments between them, and who were now on a World Tour of Salvation through Song. And I was urged to come to the Communal Hall where for four evenings only the Musical Male Quartet would lead the way to the Mercy Seat with all sixteen instruments in turn and powerful testimonies in English and French.

Pierre solemnly stared at them as they sang a last Amen, and then inquired in that loud juvenile whisper which is far more piercing than any shout, "Are they American angels?"

The Musical Quartet did not turn a hair. "No," said one with a swift wide smile. "No, not yet, not yet!"

And he threw back his head and sang, in French, "But, oh, there will be glory for me, glory for me!" The other three seized trumpet, saxophone and clarinet and joyously joined in. And across the square they marched, a great band of children capering behind.

Suddenly I felt ashamed. There was something about those four confident young evangelists, something about that quick merry smile, that set me thinking that others in fair raiment had also sung to the Lord with cheerful heart to the sound of the trumpet. So why not they?

"Oh, zut!" cried Pierre. "Chewing gum!" and started after them.

"Oh no you don't," I said and grabbed him.

"But all Americans give us boys chewing gum," howled Pierre. "They've got whole pocketfuls of it. They give it away just like that. They like giving it away! They like it, I tell you!"

"Not tonight they won't," I said. "We're late already, and it's Angélique's night out."

"Oh, okay," sighed Pierre. "Okay! Okay!"

And, sure enough, the moment we pushed open the door, out shot Angélique in her high-heeled shoes, with Pierre's supper on a tray, obviously in a great hurry to get out.

So I said that if she liked I would see Pierre safely in bed. And he tactlessly cried, "Oh, chic alors!" but Angélique, not in the least put out, said, well, if I was sure I didn't mind, and fairly tore upstairs, taking off her overall as she ran.

Pierre, of course, made his supper stretch out as long as possible; and as we at last went up the stairs, he tugged my hand. "Please," he said, "please may I see it again, just for a last treat."

"Yes," I said. "Yes."

And once again he sat on my bed and I switched off the light and let my torch shine behind the little china house. And I sat down beside him, and we both looked at it, glowing there in the dark room.

Suddenly he threw both arms round me. "Now tell me about that rabbit again," he said, "the one who ate up all the lettuces and said he hoped it would rain on the lady's best hat."

Monsieur Durand was bringing in the soup when I arrived downstairs that evening. "Ah, there you are at last!" he said. "But where is Jules Labise? Not like him to be so late."

At that very moment the door flew open and in rushed Monsieur Labise.

"Miss!" he cried. "Miss! There is news! News of your family!"

And there behind him was Monsieur Tallon, waving a letter.

8

Up the Mountains to Saint Fiacre

We all shot to our feet, exclaiming, asking questions. But Monsieur Durand quickly took us in hand.

"Calm yourselves!" he cried. "Calm yourselves. Just one moment, please!" He picked up the tureen of soup and raced it back to the kitchen. "Here, keep this warm," he rapped.

"And now, let us all sit down. Let us all have a little calm. And if Miss permits, perhaps Monsieur Tallon will read us this letter."

So we all stopped talking and sat down and looked expectantly at Monsieur Tallon; and he drew the letter from its envelope and gave a solemn little cough.

"You understand, of course," he began, "that it is my Aunt Pélagie who writes for my grandmama. And this first page is not important. It is her usual conscientious report on my grandmama's bad cough, and her own poor appetite, and her struggle to get my grandmama to swallow her nice tea made of good herbs, and all that sort of news, patati-patata, you know how these ladies talk. But here, on page two, she comes to it. Listen:

" 'Yes, dear Fortuné, Grandmama does remember the family you are interested in, the Durands who once kept the Café-Restaurant des Monuments de Nîmes. They had two children, twins, a girl and a boy. The girl married most suitably, but the boy went off to foreign parts, England, Grandmama thinks, and married a girl there whom nobody knew a thing about, entirely against his parents' wishes. But alas, dear Fortuné, how often . . .'

"M'm," said Monsieur Tallon, flicking over the page, "then my Aunt Pélagie indulges in her page and a half of sermon. She is that sort of aunt. But here, on this page, she returns to the point once more.

"'And now I must tell you, dear Fortuné, that Grandmama has just remembered that these Durands sold their business to a Madame Goddet, whose husband drank all the profits so they said. And these Durands retired to the country, to a little village in the Gard called Saint Fiacre. Grandmama says she is absolutely certain of the name because of her brother Antoine, who was your Great-uncle Antoine, of course, the one who became an Inspector of the Academy. He once taught in the school up there; it was his very first job, of course. Grandmama says it is a very small place, lost in the mountains; but your Great-uncle Antoine used to say they made an excellent little wine up there.'

"And the rest," said Monsieur Tallon, folding up the letter, "is my Aunt Pélagie's opinion of the wicked price of wine and of the Government for allowing it. I hardly think it will interest you. No, no, don't thank me. It was a pleasure, I assure you, a very real pleasure. And now if you will excuse me, I must get back to my dinner and my wife."

He paused in the doorway. "Miss will perhaps go up there to Saint Fiacre?"

"But of course!" cried Monsieur Durand before I had time to open my mouth. "Certainly she will, thanks to you! And we will let you know how she gets on, of course."

"Good!" said Monsieur Tallon. "You see, my wife is suffocating with curiosity about all this. And, well, naturally, I'm very interested, too."

"Of course you are," said Monsieur Durand. "We all are!"

It was true. They were all interested, so warmly interested that they straightway swept me off my feet. They took it for granted that I wouldn't want to waste a moment, that I would want to rush straight off to Saint Fiacre. They got out timetables. They argued about trains and buses. And by the time dinner was over they had arranged everything for me. Everything.

Angélique was to call me at six-thirty sharp the next morning, so that I could catch, in comfort, the seven-thirty train from Nîmes to a small town called Alais, which, it seemed, was a hole of a place, smothered in coal-dust. But I would not have to endure this long, less than ten minutes in fact, and then I was to board the bus bound for a village called Castillon-under-the-Mountain.

At Castillon-under-the-Mountain I was to descend from this bus and take a little refreshment outside the Café of the Faithful Friends, keeping both eyes wide open for another bus, the one that went up to Saint Fiacre. And on no account was I to miss this bus—it only ran twice a week.

Then once up in Saint Fiacre I was to have something substantial to eat, and then go straight to the presbytery and ask to see Monsieur le Curé. Yes, definitely, he was the man to see. A village priest always knew everybody. And I was to say: "Monsieur le Curé, I am Miss Dorothy Durand from England. I have reason to suppose that my French grandparents, Monsieur and Madame Marius Durand, retired to this village some fifty years ago. Will you have the kindness to direct me to them?"

And Monsieur Durand called to Angélique to bring in the coffee; and they all sat back to take satisfied breath.

"But listen," I then managed to say at last. "Do listen. If my grandparents are still alive, why, they will be well over ninety. I hardly think it possible."

"Up there," cried Monsieur Labise, "up there, my dear Miss, in those mountains, everything is possible! With all that good mountain air, that excellent little wine, people live just as long as they like!"

"In any case," said Madame Muraton, "they will be able to tell you what happened to their daughter, your Aunt What's her-name, yes, yes, Mariette-Louise, of course. They'll certainly know what happened to her. In little villages like that they have very long memories. You'll see! Now let us check up on those buses again."

That night, before I went up to my room, I asked Monsieur Durand for my bill. He looked quite taken aback.

"But, Miss," he said, "you are coming back, no?"

"Oh yes," I said. "Of course I am. In fact I am going to ask if I may leave my large suitcase here with you. I shall only need the small one."

His face lit up again. "Of course!" he said. "With pleasure."

And when I came down next morning, small suitcase in hand, ready to set out, there he was, waiting for me, with little Pierre.

"Me, I got up early, too," cried Pierre. "Papa said I could go to the market with him. And we've brought you back something special. I paid half, didn't I, Papa? Look, look! They bring good luck!"

There, by the side of my great cup of coffee, was a bunch, a most beautiful bunch of lilies of the valley.

Then they both went with me to the bus-stop; and Monsieur Durand shook hands with me, and Pierre kissed me on both cheeks. As the bus turned the corner, I could see them, still standing there, waving and calling, "Pleasant journey! Good luck!"

Then I found a couple of safety-pins in my hand-bag and carefully pinned my lilies of the valley on my coat, and when I looked up, there was the conductor, hat on the back of his head, hand outstretched, saying patiently, "Perhaps now Madame will be good enough to spare a moment to pay the fare?"

The timetable so carefully planned for me went like clockwork.

I got out of the train at Alais, and it certainly was a grimy little town—a depot for the coal that is mined in the mountains all about it, so I was told.

And I straightway got into the bus for Castillon-under-the-Mountain.

It was a wonderful ride. I had never set eyes on high mountains before, and there I was riding into a deep valley of the Cevennes, the lower slopes planted with little vines—long straight rows of them. And towering above these slopes rose the mountains, harshly majestic, almost frightening, great purple shadows drifting across them.

Castillon-under-the-Mountain turned out to be a very long, straggling village, but the bus stopped right opposite the Café of the Faithful Friends. And I got out with my suitcase, crossed the road, and sat down, as instructed, at one of the little tables on the pavement outside, keeping both eyes open for my next bus.

Then, also as instructed, I called for a little refreshment. And there I sat, waiting for it, looking up at the mountains.

The air was very warm and full of the scent of rosemary, thyme and wild lavender. There were great patches of them blooming on every slope. Behind me was an ancient twisted fig tree, I could see the small green figs forming on it; and from the vineyards on the hillside before me drifted a strange heavy fragrance. And I remembered again the lovely old words that my Aunt Kate had taught so many children to say in the spring:

> *For, lo, the winter is past,*
> *The rain is over and gone;*
> *The flowers appear on the earth,*
> *The time of the singing of birds is come,*
> *And the voice of the turtle*
> *Is heard in our land;*
> *The fig tree putteth forth her green figs,*
> *And the vines with the tender grape*
> *Give a good smell.*

And it was indeed a good smell, the scent of the sap itself, I thought, rising warm and eager in every young green shoot.

And I wished Aunt Kate could have known all this.

Then suddenly, I cannot explain it, but she seemed very near, very glad that I was sitting there, thinking of her, in that lovely scented place.

"By the way," I asked when the girl brought out my coffee, "in which direction is Saint Fiacre?"

"Up there, Madame," said the girl and pointed skywards.

And up there, very high up there, I could just make out the tiny spire of a church and a huddle of houses.

"My goodness!" I said. "Quite a climb!"

"Indeed it is, Madame! Polyte can't get his bus up there at all in the winter. Ah! Here he comes!"

Round the bend of the road rattled a battered bus, and down from the high driving seat jumped the driver, shouting for a coffee and a little glass to go with it. As he passed me, I said, "Monsieur, is this the bus to Saint Fiacre?"

"Yes, Madame," he said, "please heaven that is, and if she doesn't have one of her little seizures on the way, of course."

So I paid for my coffee and climbed into the waiting bus. There were half a dozen or so people inside, and they all looked at me with the frankest interest. It was clear that strangers with suitcases did not travel up to Saint Fiacre every day of the week.

But presently an old woman, with a big basket at her

feet, put her head out of the window and shouted, "Oh, come on there, Polyte! Don't take all day again!"

To which the driver called back that he didn't have a cast-iron throat, so give a poor devil a chance to swallow his coffee; and, anyhow, why the hurry? This wasn't America, was it?

The old lady sternly replied she wasn't interested in America, or Polyte's throat, but in the valuable sitting of eggs in her basket. If Polyte insisted on taking his usual time, her broody hen might well lose all her maternal instincts, so would he kindly hurry for once.

Out swaggered Polyte, climbed up, gave a deafening blast on his klaxon, and off we rattled.

I shall never forget it, never! We climbed up to Saint Fiacre in a series of hairpin bends. On one side, the towering mountains; on the other—a sheer drop, a yawning precipice. No comforting railings, no safe little walls—nothing! One false swerve—and we were over.

But Polyte charged up and on as if he had bought that road, right in the middle, and round every blind bend at the double. And I clung to my seat, praying we would not meet anything charging down from Saint Fiacre; and my hair fairly stood on end when Polyte suddenly swerved round, held out a grimy hand and said: "Té! I forgot to take Madame's fare!"

I fought down a wild desire to shriek, "Turn round! Don't take your eyes off that road!" and as I feverishly paid up, Polyte remarked, "Stranger, aren't you? Well, you'll find everything very tame and quiet up here, I can tell you."

I thought wildly of a trick rider I had once seen hurtling

round and round the Wall of Death on a motor-cycle—
an amateur he was, a mere beginner compared with
Polyte and his bus. He, at least, could see where he was
going! He, at least, knew he had his Wall of Death to
himself.

But at long long last, we rattled round the last bend,
bounced out on a cobbled road and shuddered to a halt
on a silent, deserted market-place.

"Saint Fiacre!" announced Polyte.

"Thank you," I said, and took up my suitcase and
sedately climbed down.

Polyte turned to his other passengers. "She's English,
of course," I heard him say. And something in his voice
implied that this explained everything, the English being
an odd lot given to jogging round unlikely places, little
suitcases at the ready in their hands.

Then off they went, every head still turned to gaze at
me standing there on the market-square of Saint Fiacre.

It certainly was the quietest place; church on one side,
café on the other, and huddled close about them some
tall gaunt houses, every shutter closed against the sun.
I looked round me, but there wasn't a soul about, not
even a cat.

"Must be somebody living here," I told myself, and
I crossed the road to the "Café des Cevennes and of the
Saint Maries of the Sea. Proprietor, Aristide Ginoux.
Repasts at all hours." All of which was painted in block
capitals on the pink-washed walls.

I pushed aside the bead curtain, walked in, and asked
the very surprised gentleman behind the zinc-topped bar
if I could have a repast—an omelette perhaps, and some

coffee. He said certainly, and yelled an order to somebody shuffling about in the kitchen. Then I asked if he had any rooms for travellers, and the gentleman, more surprised than ever, said, well, not as a rule because precious few travellers ever came that far, but he could manage one at a pinch. But, of course, he would have to ask for a little time to turn out a few things and make up a bed. I said there was no hurry; in fact there was plenty of time, as I was going over to have a word with Monsieur le Curé after I'd had my repast.

Then I remarked that the houses in Saint Fiacre seemed to me to be very tall, unusually tall, I thought. And the gentleman, delighted to find me a chatty sort, gave up pretending to polish his zinc bar, and came over and sat down with me. He said he was Monsieur Aristide Ginoux, as perhaps I had guessed; and that, yes, their houses were indeed very tall. They had been built that way during the bad old days of their religious wars. Maybe I had heard of these religious wars of theirs. Saint Fiacre, being fiercely Catholic, was, of course, on the worst possible terms with Saint Hippolyte, a village just over the mountain where they were all savagely Protestant. And so, from time to time, they used to do their religious best to wipe each other out. At moments like that, said Monsieur Ginoux, a tall house came in very handy. One bolted one's door, grabbed one's gun, raced to the top storey, leaned out of one's window, and let them have it.

And Monsieur Ginoux was proud to tell me Saint Fiacre always gave as good as it got from those hell-bound heretics over at Saint Hippolyte. Nowadays, of course, they had given up trying to convert each other.

At this point a voice from the kitchen called that my omelette was ready. Monsieur Ginoux went to get it, and set it before me with a yard or so of bread, a great dish of butter, and a carafe of wine.

"You'll have your coffee afterwards, of course," he said, and sat down once more to get on with the conversation.

He said he didn't want to give me the wrong impression. He himself didn't go to church all that much. He left such matters to his wife. By the way, she'd be sorry she had missed me. She was down at the river doing the washing. Now she was pious enough for both of them he could tell me. For instance, this café of theirs had been a straightforward "Café of the Cevennes" when they took it over. But no, she had insisted on having "and of the Saint Maries of the Sea" painted up on the wall as well. And I could work out just how much that pious gesture had cost him at fifty francs a letter.

So I was going over to see Monsieur le Curé, was I? went on Monsieur Ginoux. Well, I'd find him amiable enough. Everybody liked him, even the schoolmaster, and perhaps I knew what schoolmasters were: ardent free-thinkers, the whole pack of them. Funny, though, when one considered it, the way these free-thinkers just couldn't tolerate any brand of thinking save their own.

But Monsieur le Curé now, he got on with everyone. He was not, however, what Monsieur Ginoux would term outstanding. Not like the priest they'd had when Monsieur Ginoux was a boy. Now he *was* a character. Right out of the ordinary. He even bought himself an ancient motor car, perched high on four large wheels, with brass lamps, in which he chugged round visiting the parishioners on distant farms. And sometimes he would take his sister with him, just for the ride. Now this sister, Mademoiselle Virginie, was a determined spinster if ever there was one. One only had to look at her to be convinced of her irreproachable character. All the same, when Mademoiselle Virginie went out with Monsieur le Curé, a large notice always dangled on the back of the car: "Cette demoiselle est ma soeur. This lady is my sister", just in case they passed strangers with deplorable minds.

Monsieur Ginoux then took a cup of coffee with me, put on his straw hat, and insisted on taking me over to the presbytery—another tall, gaunt house to one side of the church. A thin acid-looking woman opened the door, asked me to step in, and promptly slammed the door behind me, leaving poor Monsieur Ginoux outside on the doorstep.

I followed her into a very clean bleak little room, with white-washed walls, a polished table, four chairs set neatly about it, a desk in one corner and a stove in the other.

"Wait here, please," she said, "Monsieur le Curé won't be a moment. He's been out in the garden spraying the vines. So you must allow him the time to wash his hands thoroughly—the stuff they use is very poisonous."

I said, of course I would, and sat down to wait. But almost immediately Monsieur le Curé came hurrying in —a round little man, with shrewd humorous eyes. He offered me a damp pink hand and said, "So sorry to keep you waiting! Séraphine, my housekeeper, thought I would poison you if I shook hands without washing first! But do sit down. I'm so very glad to see you. I was hoping we would meet. Oh yes, I knew you were here. We all quickly know when a stranger steps off Polyte's bus. But let me offer you something—a glass of 'pastis' perhaps? No? Then perhaps a little later. Now tell me, what may I have the pleasure of doing for you?"

I told him that I was hoping he might be able to give me some information about my French grandparents, Marius Durand and his wife, who had come to live in Saint Fiacre, or so I had reason to believe, some fifty years ago.

He said, "Durand? Um, Durand?" Strangely enough, believe it or not, there was not a single Durand in the whole parish of Saint Fiacre. But there, he had only been up here for the last seventeen years. And he unlocked his desk and took out two large registers, and these clearly showed that no Durands had been born, married or buried in Saint Fiacre for the past hundred years.

"Ah, but we will not give up so easily as that," said Monsieur le Curé. "Official records, though necessary, are not everything, as Holy Church Herself so sensibly teaches. We will now consult Séraphine. She has lived here all her life. Séraphine! Séraphine!"

In came Séraphine so abruptly that, well, she simply must have been just outside the door; and she immediately said, oh yes, a Monsieur Marius Durand and his wife *had* come to Saint Fiacre, fifty-one years ago last Easter it was, the year she had made her First Confession, that's why she remembered it so plainly. But they hadn't stayed long, two or three years maybe, the winters were too much for the old lady's chest. Terrible chest she had. You could hear it wheezing all over the church. So they packed up and went to live with their married daughter.

"But where? Where?" implored Monsieur le Curé. "Where?"

"I was coming to that," said Séraphine, tartly refusing to be hustled. "I was just about to explain that this married daughter of theirs lived in Saint Etienne, up there in the Loire. So that's where they went to live, up in Saint Etienne, with their married daughter. Her husband made ribbons there."

"Ribbons!" I said. "But I always thought Saint Etienne was a mining town."

"They also make ribbons," said Séraphine. "He made them. His name was Lombard, Baptiste Lombard. But I can't give you the address. The only person who could have given you that was old Victoire down at the post office, and she's been dead these twenty years, God rest her soul."

"Amen," agreed Monsieur le Curé hurriedly. "But think now, Séraphine, think hard! Isn't there something else, any other details, anything, any little thing at all that may help this lady? Remember she has come all the way from England to trace her family!"

"No," said Séraphine, "that's all there is to tell. That's all anybody here in Saint Fiacre could truthfully tell. So there's no point in my standing here thinking. If there's nothing else, I'll go and ring the bell for Vespers." And out she stalked.

"The good God in His Wisdom," said Monsieur le Curé, "created some women full of virtue but tart like quinces. I do not know what they do over there in England, but here in France they all become housekeepers to priests like me. Oh, the most efficient housekeepers, I assure you! We would be lost without them. You will come to Vespers, of course?"

So I went to Vespers; and Séraphine had done more than ring the bell, she had also spread the news. Every head turned, and there was quite a ripple of interest as I walked into the cool dark little church and took a seat near the door.

There was a great musty prayer book on the ledge in front of me, so I opened it and tried to follow the service.

"Deus, in adjutorium meum intende," intoned Monsieur le Curé. "Lord, come to my help."

"Domine, ad adjuvandum me festina," sharply came in Séraphine, shrilly leading all the rest of us. "Oh Lord, make speed to help me!"

Séraphine, I thought, admitted no dilly-dallying even from Providence.

But very humbly in my heart I cried Amen.

At the end of the service Monsieur le Curé turned from the altar and came hurrying towards me. Please, please, would I, could I, play a piece on the harmonium?

I looked at his eager kindly face, and I hated to refuse. I said I hadn't played a harmonium for years, that honestly, I was no musician.

He said, oh, that didn't matter. Neither were they. But they did so enjoy a little music when they had someone there who could play. Something quite simple would do —an English hymn maybe. And he led me to the little harmonium as if I were Harriet Cohen herself.

I sat down, wishing I were a strong-minded woman who knew how to say no, desperately trying to think of something to play.

Then suddenly as I touched the keys I thought of Mrs. Penny, her face shining with dear delight as I played hymns to her of a Sunday night. Instantly all my silly stiffness fell from me, and I began to play her favourite hymn —"All Things Bright and Beautiful". A little wheezy maybe, the pedals were awkward, but I managed it. I even managed a great Amen.

When I looked up, there was Monsieur le Curé standing by my side. "Thank you," he said. "Oh, thank you! It was quite lovely. What was it called?"

I told him it was a hymn that little children loved to sing, and I translated the title as best I could.

"Toutes choses belles et radieuses," I called it.

"Toutes choses belles et radieuses!" echoed Monsieur le Curé, his voice full of wonder. "Why, I had no idea the English sang so joyously to the Lord! 'Toutes choses belles et radieuses.' Well! Well!

"But now," he said, "will you please come outside. Séraphine has a suggestion that may interest you."

9

With the Scarlet Wolves to Saint Etienne

To my surprise there was a small crowd waiting for me in the sunshine outside, and Séraphine, very much in charge, came straight to the point.

"Miss," she said, "I have been having a word with Aristide Ginoux here, and he has an idea that seems to make sense."

She didn't add "for once in his life". Her voice left us in no doubt about that.

Monsieur Ginoux grinned and said, "Well, Miss, after you left, I suddenly remembered this football match down at Castillon this afternoon."

He paused, and I felt I was expected to say something enthusiastic. So I said, "Really?"

"Yes," went on Monsieur Ginoux; "amateurs, of course, but real live wires both sides—the Blue Stars of Castillon and District versus, listen to this, Miss, versus the Scarlet Wolves of Saint Etienne! Yes, Miss, Saint Etienne, up there in the Loire! So when I heard Séraphine telling everybody you were anxious to trace your family up there, I said, 'Well, what could be simpler? Why doesn't this English lady go down to Castillon and meet these Scarlet Wolves? Maybe one of them will be able to give her news of this Baptiste Lombard she's so interested in!' "

And Monsieur Ginoux, very gratified at the murmur of approval from the crowd, spread eloquent hands, rather like a conjuror who has pulled a remarkably fine rabbit from his hat.

"Well," I said, "this is kind of you!"

"Not at all," said Séraphine. "It's the least a Christian could do. Especially when one has a poster about it stuck on one's door. But there is no time to waste if you are to get down to Castillon today. Any minute now and that lunatic of a Polyte will be back with his bus. We'd better cross over and wave to him to stop."

Sure enough, we had just moved over to the Café des Cevennes et des Saintes Maries de la Mer when across the market square bumped Polyte's bus. So we all yelled and waved; and Polyte, very astonished, drew up; and I shook hands with as many of the crowd as I could manage, and in I got.

Suddenly I remembered something. And I stuck my head out of the window and called, "Oh, Monsieur Ginoux! I haven't paid you for my lunch! And I'd better take my suitcase, hadn't I? I won't be able to get back here today, shall I?"

"Grand Dieu, non!" cried Monsieur Ginoux. "Polyte, just you wait a moment." And bolted inside to get my suitcase.

This gave me a chance to shake hands with Monsieur le Curé and Séraphine once more and I promised faithfully I would let them know how I got on. Then Monsieur Ginoux came racing out with my suitcase and handed it through the window; and as I opened my purse to pay him, Séraphine hissed, "You only had an omelette, of course, Miss!"

I wondered how she knew, and I said, well, there was also the coffee and the bread and butter. And Monsieur Ginoux gave Séraphine a dirty look, and said one hundred and fifty francs would cover everything including the tax, which some people, who never put their noses outside the village, thought he extorted to line his own pockets. But as a travelled, intelligent woman, I, of course, would know better. We shook hands warmly on this, and Polyte, very impatient, inquired, "Tell me, is everything settled now?"

"Yes, thank you," I said. And as we rattled off, I leaned out of the window and called once more, "Thank you! Thank you!" And they all waved, and Monsieur le Curé pulled a large red check handkerchief from his pocket and waved that too, crying, "Au revoir! Come back one day!"

Then Polyte, holding his hand out for the fare, said, "Pécaïre! You didn't stay long!"

"No," I apologised. "You see, I heard about this football match down at Castillon. . . ."

"Bouffre!" cried Polyte, and turned to the other four passengers. "Did you hear that! Now will you believe what I tell you about the English! They are all crazy about football, even the women!"

I did not contradict him. I didn't dare, for if Polyte charging up to Saint Fiacre was hair-raising, Polyte spanking down to Castillon was positively blood-curdling. And as we took the first bend on two wheels at the double, Polyte lit a cigarette, blew the smoke through his nose, and said, "Me, I could do this blasted trip with my eyes shut!"

I said I wished I could, too, and with that I shut my eyes and let the mountains above and the precipices below go hurtling by, and prayed that Polyte's brakes were in better shape than the rest of his bus.

They were, for twenty minutes or so later we drew up with an almighty screech right opposite the Café of the Faithful Friends. And Polyte turned and said, "How's that for time, eh? Nothing short of one of those jets of yours would have got you here for the first half, but I've managed it in record time for the second. The field's over there, behind the school."

I thanked him and strode briskly off, trying to look the picture of the British sporting-woman, determined not to miss one moment of the rest of the match. I felt I owed that much to Polyte.

But all the while, inside, I was feverishly wondering how on earth I was to introduce myself to a French football team, wondering if they would think that I was slightly—well, peculiar, to say the least of it.

In fact I had to take myself firmly in hand. "Dorothy Durand," I said to myself, "don't you dare consider bolting! Kindly remember all those friendly people in Nîmes and up there in Saint Fiacre, all falling over themselves to help you trace your family. You face up to this football team. They can't eat you!"

And striving to feel cool and sure of myself, I turned into the field behind the church. Immediately a brass band massed under a great tree broke into a lively polka.

Oh, not for me, but to entertain the hundred or so spectators now sitting or strolling about on the grass during the interval. So I took a deep breath and spoke to a gentleman leaning against one of the goal-posts. I asked what the score was, as I had unfortunately missed the first half. He said, ah, pity, pity! It had been palpitating, absolutely palpitating! Three all.

Then he looked at me again, and asked, "Madame is English, no?"

"Yes," I said, and decided again that there must be something British in my voice that stuck out a mile.

"Thought so," said the gentleman. "Tell me, Madame, have you ever seen Arsenal play?"

"Oh yes," I said; but I didn't add that I was only ten at the time and that I had spent the match hopping up and down the steps of the grandstand sucking a stick of rock and asking Bill Penny if it wasn't time to go home yet.

It was the look on the gentleman's face that silenced me. He was gazing at me as if I had admitted that I was first cousin to royalty itself.

"Pray come with me, Madame," he said. "You must have a good seat."

He led me across the field to a bench, close to the brass band, and introduced me to all the gentlemen sitting there.

"This lady," he said, "is from England. She watches Arsenal play!" And his voice implied that everywhere that Arsenal went there I was sure to go.

The gentlemen, very impressed, politely moved up and made room for me on the bench. And I sat down feeling the shadiest humbug—bluffing my way like this into honest football circles.

Mercifully, before they had time to ask any questions, the whistle blew, and the Blue Stars and the Scarlet Wolves were off, tearing down the field at the gallop.

Now I cannot say if they played good football. I just wouldn't know.

But as spectators, we were magnificent! We bawled, we cheered, we hissed, we implored, we deplored, we howled our opinion of the referee—all at the tops of our voices. And every time a goal was scored we turned to the brass band and yelled "Musique! Musique!" And the brass band would strike up, and we would smack each other on the back, or shake our fists, and somebody would simply *have* to dash out on the field to embrace the hero, and the referee, tearing his hair, would chase him off, and—well, it was palpitating all right, absolutely palpitating.

When the last whistle blew, we all rose to our feet, and the brass band played for its life—it had to, to make itself heard—whilst we cheered and clapped and roared our approval as the Scarlet Wolves shook hands with the vanquished Blue Stars in the most gentlemanly way. And I turned to the delirious gentleman on my right, who was definitely on the side of Saint Etienne, and I congratulated him, and said I was wondering if it would be possible for me to have a word with the Scarlet Wolves before they left.

His face lit up with pleasure. Nothing, it seemed, could be easier. He, himself, was from Saint Etienne. In fact he had brought the team down to Castillon on his bus over there. And if I would be at the Café of the Faithful Friends in, say, a little quarter of an hour, just time for them to change, he would be enchanted to introduce me to the boys.

So I strolled round Castillon-under-the-Mountain for a quarter of an hour, seeing absolutely nothing, very cool and casual outside, but very hot and bothered within, wondering just what to say, what they would think.

But I need not have worried. When I pushed aside the long bead curtains and stepped into the Café of the Faithful Friends, there they were, sitting round a long table, waiting for me. And they all rose to their feet, smiling; and before I had time to think, there I was shaking hands all round in the friendliest way. Then I was requested to sit down by the side of the captain; and he got up and said, "Boys, I know I speak for us all when I say how pleased and honoured we are to have had an English lady at the match this afternoon. So let us drink first of all, not to our victory, but to Great Britain, the Mother of Football!"

He leaned down and took a bottle standing in a bucket at his feet, and I saw it was champagne. And he filled all the glasses, and they rose to their feet and drank.

"To Great Britain, the Mother of Football!"

Suddenly I felt better, much better; not nearly such a humbug. I saw with comforting, shining clarity that it was not me they were honouring, but Football, British Football.

Then I realised they were all seated again and were looking at me, clearly expecting me, the Arsenal fan, to say a few words. So I got to my feet, and, honestly, I

didn't know I had it in me, but I heard myself warmly
thanking them in the name of Great Britain; I compli-
mented them on their football; I most truthfully said I
had never enjoyed a match more in my life; I said I was
proud and happy to tell them that I had reason to believe
that I myself might have some links with their great city,
that I might have some relatives living there, called
Lombard; that, in fact, I intended to make Saint Etienne
my next port of call to make a few inquiries about these
relatives of mine; and that now, well now, I hoped more
than ever that I would have the good fortune to trace
them before I had to return to my job in England.

And to great applause I sat down, quite overcome by
my own startling eloquence.

Then straightway those warm-hearted lads began
asking questions, racking their brains, trying to recall
every Lombard they had ever met.

Presently one of them banged on the table for silence.
"Listen," he said, "they wouldn't be in ribbons by any
chance?"

My heart stood still.

"Yes," I said. "More than likely."

"Well," he said, "I've an aunt who is in ribbons and
she lives opposite two ladies called Lombard, about your
age they'd be. Catherine and Françoise. They're both in
ribbons."

"But what is their father's name?" I asked, my voice
suddenly very hoarse.

"Baptiste," he said. "Baptiste Lombard. There's a
little brass plate on their door: Baptiste Lombard. He's
been dead years now, but they've never taken it off."

"It sounds too good to be true," I said. "But if you will give me the address I'll most certainly call and see them."

"We can do better than that," he cried. "If there is nothing to keep you here in Castillon, we'll take you right there. Plenty of room in the bus, eh, boys?"

"Oh, thank you," I stuttered. "But . . ."

"Good!" he said, and before I had time to grasp what was happening to me he had seized my suitcase and I was swept out of the Café of the Faithful Friends and up into their bus—on my way to Saint Etienne!

And it was not only my very first glass of champagne that now soared to my head on shining carefree wings; no, no, it was a growing certainty that all this was quite beyond my control. Otherwise, why was I there, sitting in this bus, heading for Saint Etienne . . . ?

Then I admitted to my more level-headed self that Séraphine would not altogether have approved of the way Providence was making such rollicking speed to help me—at least sixty miles an hour along a long straight road, with all the Scarlet Wolves hanging from the windows playing mouth-organs, or singing at the tops of their voices, and blowing kisses to every girl and woman under sixty we passed on the way.

Presently they brought out what they called a little "break-crust"—just a small snack, I gathered—a couple of hard-boiled eggs each, some large slices of ham, a fine chunk of cheese, and, of course, half a dozen bottles.

"Oh, but we insist! You must have a glass," they cried. "Listen, Miss; this is none of your push-the-boys-to-crime stuff! Monsieur le Curé buys this little wine for the choirboys' outing, it's so soft and innocent!"

Then the sun went down, and the stars came out and danced over the straight white road; and the Scarlet Wolves, very mellowed by the "break-crust" and the soft, innocent wine, grew a little sentimental and began to croon, not about the moon and June, but about the lilacs ablooming both purple and white and the cruel loves who'd left them one tender spring night.

Then one by one they began to yawn; and the lad sitting by my side slid down in his seat and rested his dark head on my shoulder. "You're nice, you know," he said. "In fact I find you very nice indeed. A little like my Mama. Her eyes laugh, too." And with that he put a fond filial arm round my waist, yawned, and fell fast asleep.

Then somebody still awake up by the driver struck up a ballad about a poor faithful gentleman waiting for his loved one inside a café, and the clock tick-tocked, and the flies flick-flocked, but still the gentleman waited. And waited. And WAITED!

I laughed, not very loudly, because of the lad sleeping on my shoulder. But the singer heard me. "Ah!" he said. "You just wait till the last verse. It's a peach!"

I didn't say so, but it wasn't his song that was making me laugh. I had suddenly thought of Miss Clarkson, the headmistress of the modern school, how her eyes would have popped from her head to see me sitting there, improving my French, a Scarlet Wolf asleep on my shoulder, one arm about my waist.

Then I laughed again, for the singer had come to the last verse, and it *was* a peach, a very ripe peach, and I had a feeling Miss Clarkson would not have appreciated it, that she would NOT have been amused.

Then the singer fell asleep, too; and now the miles slid by in warm, drowsy silence.

But I was wide-awake, one side of me excited, full of hope; the other urging me to be sensible, warning me that this might well turn out the wildest of goose-chases, that there were thousands of Baptiste Lombards in France, maybe almost as many as Marius Durands. But it was no use. I could almost hear my heart singing with excitement, especially when the driver turned and shouted, "Come on, boys! Wake up! We're nearly there! Look, Miss, there it is, down there."

There, at the foot of the long hill down which we were now speeding, twinkled a thousand lights, the lights of a great city, the lights of Saint Etienne.

The Scarlet Wolves woke up and yawned and stretched, and reached for their coats. And I began to say that I would be grateful if they would drop me at a quiet little hotel, that I really could not call on anyone at this time of night. "Why, it's almost midnight," I said. "I ought to call on these ladies tomorrow I think."

But they would not hear of it. "No, no," they said. "If these ladies are your cousins, they will be very upset if you don't go straight there. Suppose they *are* in their beds! They won't mind. They'll be glad to get up. We're like that in Saint Etienne, Miss! No side, no ceremony, everything straight from the heart. Yes, that's how we are. No, no! We'll take you right there."

"They'll just *have* to be your cousins," said the dark-haired boy by my side. "I can't go home and make my mama cry, you know! Very tender-hearted, my mama!"

So down into Saint Etienne we drove, past brightly lit cafés, people still sitting outside in the cool night air, up a wide avenue, along a very straight narrow road, and into a quiet street.

"Number seventy-seven you said, didn't you, Claudius?" asked the driver. "Well, here it is, Miss."

He drew up, and I got out, walked across the pavement, and rang the bell under the neat little brass plate: Baptiste Lombard. Behind me, the Scarlet Wolves, suddenly very silent, leaned from every window. For a moment the whole world stood still.

Then the door opened. And there stood a plump little woman in dressing-gown and slippers, dark hair rolled up in curlers.

"Mon Dieu!" she gasped, looking past me at the bus outside, all the Scarlet Wolves leaning from it.

"Mademoiselle Lombard?" I asked, my throat very dry.

"Mais oui, Madame," she said.

"Please forgive me for calling so late," I said, "but my name is Durand, Dorothy Durand. I live in England, but my father was French. His name was Marius. He came from Nîmes. He had a twin-sister called Mariette-Louise, and I'm wondering if by any chance your mother . . ."

My voice trailed away. I could not say another word.

"No!" she cried. "No!" and flung up both her arms. "Catherine! Catherine! Come here! Come quickly! You won't believe it, but our cousin is here, the daughter of our Uncle Marius . . . all the way from England."

And she flung both her arms about me and kissed me.

Down the stairs came a tall thin woman, arms outstretched, crying, "But come in! Come in, please!" And from behind us came a great roaring cheer.

"These gentlemen," I stammered, "have been most kind. They brought me here. . . ."

"Then they must come in," cried my short plump cousin. "They must take something!"

But the Scarlet Wolves politely declined, said their families would be sitting up waiting for them, and before I had time to thank them properly, off they drove, still waving and cheering as they went.

"Oh, the neighbours won't mind," said my tall thin cousin, reading my thoughts, "not when we tell them the news. But come in, please come in. Oh, you are welcome, so welcome!"

And she, too, flung her arms about me and kissed me.

And with my heart beating very hard I followed my cousins up the stairs.

10

My Cousins, Françoise and Catherine

I know it sounds ridiculous, but the next morning I was
half afraid to wake up properly, half afraid all this just
could not have happened to me.

And I lay there for a while, remembering how I had
followed my cousins up the stairs and into a neat little
living-room.

And then a terrible shyness seized me. I longed to talk,
to explain; but no words came, till I saw the framed
photograph hanging on the wall in front of me, a photograph I knew so well, the one of Mariette-Louise and her
friend Alexandrine, and behind them, smiling at me, my
father, and the tall thin young man with the fine moustache, *their* father, of course, Baptiste Lombard.

I pointed to it. And laughed, my eyes full of tears. And
they laughed, too. And the ice was broken, thank God.

Soon there we were sitting round the table looking at
my family album that I had brought with me in my suitcase, and they brought out their family album, and we
laughed and cried to see the same, the very same photographs in them both.

They told me that our grandparents and their mother,
my Aunt Mariette-Louise, had died, all three, in one

nightmare week, of the terrible influenza that swept like a plague over Europe in the winter of 1918.

"We have always lived very quietly," said Catherine. "Just making our ribbons, and looking after Papa, till he died last December."

"Last December!" I said, and told them about my Aunt Kate.

"But this won't do!" cried Françoise presently. "Sitting here blowing our noses, when we should be celebrating! Catherine, get out the best cups. I will make some tea. It will calm us all."

And I watched, fascinated, as she took a jug, put in a spoonful of tea, poured on a tablespoonful of cold water, let it soak for a while, and then filled up with hot water.

"There," she said, as she poured out this calming brew. "Taste me that."

"Wonderful!" I said, and drank it down. And it *was* wonderful. Everything was wonderful, so wonderful that now I was half afraid to wake up in case it was all a dream.

But no, there I was, in a tiny neat bedroom in my cousins' flat in Saint Etienne. Those were my clothes on the chair; there on the table by my side was my family album.

And now there was a lovely smell of coffee on the air, and I could hear someone tiptoeing round outside. So I pulled on my dressing-gown and opened the door; and there were my two cousins laying the table for breakfast, and crying, "Ah, good day, Dor-o-tee! Did you sleep well? But sit down, sit down! No need to dress! The coffee is ready!"

Yes, it was wonderful. It was home. I could feel it in the very air. And with my heart very full and warm, I pulled up a chair and sat down to breakfast.

"Poor Dor-o-tee!" laughed Françoise. "She now sees us in the searching light of day. So I have made the coffee very good and strong."

I said they were exactly as I dearly hoped they would be.

"Ah well," said Françoise, pouring hot milk and coffee into three enormous cups, "we, alas, have no choice about our looks. I am the image of our maman, round as a cabbage, but not so dull, I hope.

"And our Catherine there, is just like Papa—thin, tall and elegant, like a stick of asparagus. And exasperatingly intelligent! I tell you, Dor-o-tee, she positively adores being educated. She dotes on these lectures on anything and anybody. Oh, · frightfully well-informed, our Catherine, I can tell you!"

Catherine, cutting the long loaf into chunks, said of all the nonsense, and that she enjoyed talking, too, when given the chance, and that she had lain awake last night thinking how extraordinary it was, how fortunate, that I had turned up at this very time. I simply could not have come at a better moment. They, too, were about to treat themselves to a holiday! They swore this was true, that indeed this was why they had been up so late last night, tidying up their workroom. It seemed that they still made ribbons at home, just as their father, and his father, and every other Lombard before him had done for generations.

"Look out of the window," they said. And when I looked, I saw that both sides of the road were lined with tall flat houses with great uncurtained windows.

"This is the Ribbon Quarter of Saint Etienne," said Catherine. "And ribbon-making demands plenty of light."

"There aren't so many of us left now," said Françoise. "The young people won't take it up. Takes too long to learn. They want to earn good money right away. And who can blame them? One is only young once. But come up and see our workroom, Dor-o-tee."

She led the way up another flight of stairs and unlocked the door of a large room, very light and airy; one wall was almost all window.

Four great looms of polished wood all but filled this room, and towered up to the ceiling, supporting a maze of complicated belts and strands of fine delicate silk threads that stretched down to the benches below.

"At one time," said Françoise, patting the carved post of one of the looms, "each one of these was worth a little fortune. Maman used to say, 'At least the girls are provided for. They have the looms.' But now, I don't suppose they would fetch more than the price of so much firewood."

"It's a very great pity," said Catherine quietly. "The most beautiful ribbons in the world were made on looms like these in the homes of Saint Etienne. Soon they will all be mass-produced in factories. It is never quite the same—for the people who make them, I mean. But look, Dor-o-tee, this is how they work."

She switched on the electricity, and a hundred little glass shuttles began to click-clock to and fro; and as I watched, the ribbons grew, lovely ribbons of silk, satin and velvet.

The velvet ones fascinated me even more than the others. They had a special loom of their own, fitted with sharp little razors. The ribbons looked like thick satin pads till they reached these razors, which then sliced them through, just as you would cut through a thick slice of bread to make two thinner slices. And as each pad fell apart, there within shone the velvet pile, thick, soft and lovely.

But it was exacting work, I was told, this ribbon-making at home. There were a thousand intricate details to be seen to. One had to be born in ribbons to understand everything. Then so much depended on fashion. If ribbons went out, the whole quarter tightened its belt and reached for the stocking which held the savings. All the same, there was something about ribbon-making. One groused incessantly, but one went on making them. It was in the blood, this love of ribbons.

I looked at the beautiful shining ribbons slowly growing on the tall polished looms and said, yes, I thought I understood.

"But now, enough of work!" cried Françoise, and switched off the electricity.

"Tell me, Dor-o-tee, can you ride a bicycle?"

"Why yes," I said. "At least I could once."

They both looked so pleased that I was very glad I had not added, "but I can't say I enjoyed it."

It seemed they did more than enjoy cycling—they adored it. They belonged to a small club called "The Friends of the Pedal", just a dozen or so sensible middle-aged people, so there was none of this scorching flat on one's stomach with one's head on one's handle-bars. No, no, the Friends of the Pedal went in for pleasant little jaunts in the country of a week-end, with a picnic on the grass if the weather was kind. If it wasn't, they still took their own food and had it in one of these cafés where the patron serves a bottle of wine or a cup of coffee and no dirty looks at the provisions being pulled from an honest cyclist's haversack.

And I said, of course I'd be absolutely delighted to become a Friend of the Pedal, as long as I might wobble away in the rear till I got my cycling-legs back again as it were.

And, with that, we went downstairs, washed up the breakfast things, and Françoise rushed straight off to see about borrowing a bicycle for me, Catherine went out to do some shopping, and I sat down to write some letters.

First of all I sent one of my postcards to Miss Clarkson of the modern school. "Now in Saint Etienne, staying with cousins. Lovely weather. Best wishes to all. D. Durand." And for the first time since I left England I gave my address.

Then I wrote a long letter to Monsieur le Curé of Saint Fiacre. I told him how kind the Scarlet Wolves had been to me, how they had taken me right to my cousins' home. I asked him to tell the good news to Séraphine and Monsieur Ginoux, and to thank them most warmly for all they had done to help me. Then I said that the English hymn, "Toutes choses belles et radieuses", had always held many dear memories for me, but now I should never hear it without remembering the little church of Saint Fiacre and all his courtesy and kindness. And sincerely hoping I would have the pleasure of meeting them all again one day, I remained his grateful Dorothy Durand.

Last of all, I wrote a very long letter indeed to Monsieur Durand. I told him everything, every little detail, from the moment I stepped off the train at Alais. Then I said I simply did not know how to thank him and all the "regulars"; that I could never forget the happy time I had spent in Nîmes; and that I knew I could ask him to thank everybody for me, including Monsieur Tallon, the photographer. I said that my cousins, who were also on holiday, simply insisted on my staying with them in Saint Etienne for a while, so when he had a moment, would he kindly send on my large suitcase. I then assured him that I was looking forward with real pleasure to returning to the Café-Restaurant des Monuments de Nîmes for a few days before I had to return to England. And I ended with my friendliest greetings to them all, and an affectionate message to little Pierre.

Then almost singing aloud in my new happiness, I put on a hat and set out to find a tobacconist who sold stamps; and a letter-box.

Monsieur le Curé of Saint Fiacre wrote back almost by return of post. He said he would require the gifted pen of the great Charles Dickens himself—whom he had read, but in translation, of course—to describe how Monsieur Ginoux now nightly held forth at the Café des Cevennes et des Saintes Maries de la Mer on his brilliant stratagem to help an English Milady in Search of a Family. And how Séraphine—not only to put Aristide Ginoux in his place, no, no, not only for that—this good Séraphine had lit a very tall candle on my behalf to Saint Antoine of

Padua, who, as everyone knew, was unsurpassed in finding anything for anybody, even a family.

But seriously now, all joking apart, they were all truly delighted to hear my excellent news; he was in fact going to preach a very good sermon on it on Sunday, and he begged me to accept his sentiments of respectful cordiality and his warmest good wishes for much happiness in the bosom of the family to which the good God Himself had so surely led me.

But the days went by and there was no word of reply from Monsieur Durand. And no sign of the suitcase. Oh, I was not worried about the suitcase. I knew that would turn up all right. But I did think Monsieur Durand might have dropped me a line. He had seemed so interested, so friendly. . . .

And it did not precisely soothe my ruffled feelings when I at last received a picture postcard of the Arena which said:

"All enchanted to hear good news. Very occupied at moment. Suitcase soon as possible. Cordial handshakes. Kiss from Pierre.

"M. DURAND."

I told myself not to be such a fool, but it made no difference. This was the last thing I had expected, this hasty indifferent scrawl on the back of a picture postcard. I felt more than hurt; I felt almost humiliated.

So I was more grateful than ever, if that were possible, that life with my cousins was so brisk and lively. Françoise, I quickly realised, was a most gifted talker. The most commonplace of incidents when told by her became positively enthralling. Catherine, if quieter, had a deft quick wit that kept us all chuckling. And we sensibly wasted no time at all in unprofitable silence. We not only talked all day, we often talked half through the night as well.

We began first thing in the morning as we dusted and polished their little flat—one living-room, two bedrooms, the workroom, and a dark cupboard fitted with a sink in which we washed everything—ourselves, the clothes, and the dishes. I soon got used to this; but I thought I would never get used to another dark retreat on one of the landings proudly labelled W.C., which served all three flats in the building and to which we went bearing a great iron key as if setting forth to fling open some dark medieval dungeon.

Then every day at twelve we would sit down, still talking, to the excellent meal we had taken half the morning to prepare. And we would take our respectful time over this. No bolting snacks-on-toast for my French cousins and their friends. Thrifty they most certainly were; but they all thought it necessary to spend far more on food and wine than anyone I knew in England— often as much as half their incomes, I discovered. Things I considered luxuries they thought indispensable to good living. Not only that, they all spent far more time on the job. Most women I met seemed to spend half the day over their stoves. To them the real luxuries were carpets, easy-chairs, vacuums, plumbing, new wallpaper, and paint. All this could wait; in fact it had to wait, if they were to serve the meals their families expected, the meals in which they took such pride. Homes could be shabby with dignity. Shabby meals were not to be thought of.

On the other hand, I was outraged to discover that they had all been brought up to believe that no woman across the Channel knew the first thing about cooking. When I indignantly declared that most of us could cook, in our own way, of course, and that some of us even enjoyed cooking, they always brought up our "vegetables-cooked-in-plain water". And there would be such a note of pity and scorn in their voices that I would swear that if British vegetables were fresh, they were delicious that way and that in my opinion it was a crime, for instance, to smother the delicate flavour of green peas with all their onions, their lettuce, their bouquets of thyme, parsley and bay.

They always howled this down, of course; so I would be driven back to my last line of defence—their livers! I would solemnly declare that I was staggered, absolutely staggered at the French liver. I would call attention to their newspapers, their hoardings, their chemists' shops, all blazing with cures for the liver, not to mention the endless brands of mineral-waters, the herb-teas, all guaranteed to calm their rampaging livers.

They would swear that this was a matter of temperament; that they felt things far too deeply, far too vividly, and this, of course, was extremely upsetting for any civilised liver.

And I'd say, nonsense, their exquisite cooking must also have something to do with it. They couldn't all be born liverish.

I never convinced them, of course; but a hilarious time was had by all as we argued it out. I believe that secretly they rather admired their conception of the British woman, eternally clad in stout tweeds and brogues, slapping up meals, take it or leave it, refusing to recognise more than one standard sauce, and no getting hot and bothered even about that.

Then every afternoon, come rain, come shine, and still talking of course, I was taken out to see Saint Etienne.

Now even French people will say, "But what is there to see in Saint Etienne? It's a mining-town!"

And so it is, of course. The whole city is built over the mines. As Catherine once remarked to me, it was queer when one stopped to think of it, that there, under their houses, their streets, the miners were hard at it. And they were not all Frenchmen by any means. Arabs, Poles, Italians and Greeks as well, all toiled for their bread, far from the sun, in a nationalised Pit of Babel deep below Saint Etienne.

Then there are steel-works in Saint Etienne and glass-works, and a great National Factory of Arms, where army officers hold all the key posts and no visitors are ever welcomed. And I was urged not to make the common and irritating mistake of confusing this mighty arsenal with their other great factory—the French Factory of Arms and Cycles. Now this "veritable palace of industry" warmly invites the public to call in any day and inspect the way they turn out the finest of weapons for sportsmen, bicycles that are "the graceful little queens of the road", and a bewildering variety of other articles for every possible pursuit from fishing to mountaineering.

"Oh yes," said Catherine as we limped home after inspecting all this, "down there in Nîmes they may have their Roman monuments, but we have a saying that goes 'The monuments of Saint Etienne are its factories'."

Then one day I set out alone to have a look at some old streets with names that delighted me: the Street of Frank Friendship, the Street of the Rock of the Wolf, the Street of the Smiths, the Street of the Glorious Three, the Street of Eternity—I found this last one led to the cemetery. And I was going along the Street of the Weapon Makers when I saw a woman sitting at an open window, chiselling the handle of a gun, decorating it with a delicate intricate pattern. I stopped and said I hoped she didn't mind my watching her for a moment. She said, no, not at all, with pleasure, and that at one time everybody up and down the street used to work on guns. And some lovely weapons they had turned out too, for Napoleon himself, and all the kings of France before him. And trust the kings of France to demand the finest of everything, from palaces to guns. And I really ought to go to the museum and see some of these guns for myself, real masterpieces they were, encrusted with gold, silver, ivory and mother-of-pearl.

And she put down her gun and said she would come with me to the end of the road and point out the best way to the museum.

Then Catherine belonged to a society called "The Friends of Saint Etienne", and she loved to point to an old doorway or house and say, "Now that was standing there when your Henry V and our Catherine of Valois were playing duets on their harps", or "when your

Edward III sent his bowmen to lay waste to Saint
Etienne, because even in those days we were turning
out some redoubtable weapons. We buried your bowmen
decently, of course. I can take you to the very place.
It is still called 'The Cemetery of the English', and this
was truly polite of us because at that time they went by
the name of 'God-dams'."

Oh yes, one way and another, I learned some remarkable history in Saint Etienne.

Best of all, however, I loved the evenings, the warm
friendly evenings when we just sat and talked.

One evening I shall never forget. We had been out to
supper with friends, and it was late and very warm—
far too warm to think of bed.

"Let's make a night of it," said Françoise. "Let's
be riotous. Let's have an ice-cream down on the Place
Marengo."

So we strolled on towards the Place Marengo, one of
the finest squares in Saint Etienne, and officially re-
named the Place Jean Jaurès, but nobody seemed to
bother about that, except perhaps the postman.

We sat down outside a café, ordered our ice-creams,
and sat back to watch the rest of Saint Etienne stroll
by.

In a neat little bandstand across the square a brass
band struck up something sad and wistful.

"Manon!" said Catherine immediately and began to
hum the melody.

Then two little girls came skipping along, followed
sedately by Papa and Maman.

"They're up late," I said.

"Of course!" said Françoise. "If it's too warm for us to sleep, it is also too warm for them."

As she passed us, one of the little girls gave a squeal, clasped her hands in ecstasy, and said, "Oh, Lolotte, won't it be lovely when they're here? The holidays, I mean!"

And Lolotte flung her little handbag in the air, caught it, and burst into a ditty that went:

> *Long live the holidays!*
> *Down with the punishments!*
> *On a great fire let the books drop,*
> *Fling the whole lot on the burning-hot top.*

"Mm!" said Catherine. "The rising generation is certainly more restrained than we were. Now we used to chant, 'On a great fire let the teachers flop, roast the whole lot on the burning-hot top.'"

"Ah!" said Françoise. "But teachers were different in those days. When I think of Mademoiselle Bobet, for instance . . ."

"Go on," said Catherine kindly. "Tell Dor-o-tee your Mademoiselle Bobet story. You know how you adore telling it."

She called to the waiter, ordered more ice-creams; and I turned to Françoise and said encouragingly, "Yes, what was she like, this Mademoiselle Bobet?"

11

Prize Distribution, 1907

"Mademoiselle Bobet," said Françoise slowly, "was a most remarkable person. Disciplinarian! Why, that woman did not have to open her mouth. She only had to open the door and we'd all shoot up in our little desks, backs as stiff as pokers, arms folded just so across our little flat chests.

"It was in Mademoiselle Bobet's class, by the way, that I earned my shining reputation for being a nice silent little girl."

I said, well, strive as I might, I simply could not imagine Françoise as a nice silent little girl. Not a *silent* little girl.

"In Mademoiselle Bobet's class," said Françoise with considerable hauteur, "I was as mute as a little fish. That woman did something to me. . . ."

I said I had, of course, heard of Medusa, but that I had never come across one in real life—not even in the teaching profession.

"No, no," cried Françoise. "You seem to have the wrong impression. When I got used to it, I positively revelled in my rôle of a nice silent little girl, especially when Mademoiselle Bobet paid me little compliments.

'Lucienne Frécon,' she would say, 'go and sit by quiet little Françoise Lombard!'

"You must understand that even your Medusa would have had no success with this Lucienne Frécon. Nobody could reduce *her* to silence. And the moment Mademoiselle Bobet's back was safely turned, she would stick her tongue out at me, sitting there as silent and sympathetic as the tomb; and she would hiss, 'You're nothing but a pear, Françoise Lombard, a stuck-up little pear!', or some other deadly insult.

"Yes, yes, I know we French are extraordinary. If a little girl is charming we call her a little cabbage; if she is a smug little show-off we call her a little pear. But don't blame me for it, just allow me to continue with this Lucienne Frécon. Now she knew all the classic insults, I can tell you. Presently she would toss back her long wavy mane of hair and murmur, 'And that hair of yours curls just like the Rue de Roanne!'

"This was a cruel thrust if you please, for our Rue de Roanne, as you know, runs right through Saint Etienne as straight and interesting as a ruler. And it was true, this insult! I did have hair like that—I, who longed to have curly hair, wavy hair, frizzy hair, any sort of hair except the hair that grew on my head as dull and straight as our Rue de Roanne. And it was no use plaiting it, or rolling it up in rags and enduring agonies all night long. By the time I got to school in the morning my satanic hair would be dangling about my face again as straight and lank as rainwater.

"And that year, the year I was Mademoiselle Bobet's nice silent pupil, this truly depressed me. You see, I was deeply concerned about our Distribution of Prizes. Always a red-letter day, our Distribution of Prizes, but this year it was going to be momentous. I knew in my bones that I was destined for at least one prize—the Prize for Good Conduct. It was unthinkable that Mademoiselle Bobet should nominate someone else. Why, I had not uttered one illegitimate sound all that long tedious year. First of all, I admit, I was too scared of Mademoiselle Bobet, but by now I was fairly revelling in my fine Trappist reputation. But naturally a girl has to fill her time in with something, and with Mademoiselle Bobet in charge I prudently decided it might as well be work. Oh, I don't say I shone! My arithmetic was completely undistinguished, especially when I wrestled with the financial problems of those three gentlemen who always buy three fields, one of which is five times greater than the second which is perversely only two-ninths the size of the third.

"But my spelling was sparkling, and my reading downright torrential. 'Take a breath, child! For the love of high heaven, take a breath!' Mademoiselle Bobet would implore as I cantered through the paragraphs and flew over every full stop in my anxiety to show how I could master all the hard words.

"Secretly, then, I nursed a shining hope that I might land more than the Prize for Good Conduct—I might even carry off the most glittering prize of all—the Prize for Excellence. That would teach that Lucienne Frécon!

"And so the silent days wore on until it was late July; and at long last, one Sunday, the notice appeared in both our newspapers, the *Memorial* and the *Tribune*: 'The Distribution of Prizes to the pupils of our Communal Schools for Girls will take place on Thursday, August 1st, in the Great Hall of the Bourse du Travail.'

"Instantly a thousand young voices took up the cry, 'You saw? The Prizes on Thursday! Thursday!'

"Thursday. We calculated feverishly. Three days, three short days to complete all our preparations. No use our families expostulating that there was plenty of time. We knew better. Every girl had her dress to consider, her sash, hair-ribbon, buttoned boots, and hair. Oh, above all her hair! For the Distribution of Prizes a girl's hair just had to be magnificent. We must set to work at once if we were to achieve a 'coiffure' of which we might feel proud.

"That night I lay in bed, hair tightly plaited, but with my heart as heavy as lead, raging at the cruel fate that had planted my head with hair as obstinate as the Rue de Roanne. Everything else was going to be so perfect. My summer dress was almost new. There it hung on my bedroom door, freshly laundered by Madame Brossard, Maman's friend and an expert in starch, never too much, never too little, so that the wide frills round neck, sleeves and hem rippled crisp and fresh but not in the least stiff and scratchy. In the top drawer of my cupboard there was my new sash, a present from our Tante Virginie who also made ribbons at home. A lovely sash, celestial blue, the very colour of the cloak of Our Lady of Lourdes. And long! Two and a half metres, enough to go round my waist, make a big bow and fall in two ends to the hem of my frock. And exactly matching my sash, a new hair-ribbon, also a present from Tante Virginie.

"But my hair, my miserable Rue de Roanne hair, no matter how I strove with it, it would most surely ruin all my dear elegance. And I buried my face in my pillow and wept.

"The next morning, however, I set off to school looking as business-like as the rest of my class. Every girl of us had her hair tightly scraped back in a multitude of plaits— the more numerous these plaits, the more magnificent the ultimate glory. Lucienne Frécon and those fortunate others with hair right down to their waists had tied their long plaits together, doubled them up, and secured them artistically on the tops of their heads. My paltry plaits were just bundled together in the nape of my neck, of course.

"Worse still, I knew that all my plaiting would be in vain. I saw myself at the Distribution, the only straight head in all the Great Hall of the Bourse du Travail. In my dark despair I confided in Lucienne Frécon, yes, Lucienne, that will show you how I felt.

" 'Françoise Lombard!' she giggled. 'You are a noodle. All you have to do is soak it in strong sugar-water, of course.'

"That evening then I implored Catherine to sugar-water and remake my plaits. Now I hate to say this in front of her, but Catherine was not always as sympathetic a sister as I could have desired. To my mind, she over-worked her, 'I'm five years older than you', but that Monday evening she had nothing more important to do, so she helped me dissolve lumps of sugar in a jug

of hot water till even I felt the solution was strong enough.
Then she took a comb and began operations. I tell you
I know precisely how it must feel to be scalped! No
Red Indian was ever more thorough and ruthless than
our Catherine. When she had finished, a hundred little
plaits stuck out all over my head as stiff as drumsticks
and the skin of my head was as tight as the drum. But
I knew one must suffer to be beautiful. So I suffered,
and offered up all my sufferings to my patron saint, adding,
'So please for one day let it stay in! Please don't let it
all drop out! Please!'

"Tuesday and Wednesday dragged by, and, of course,
no comb came near any head in our class. And I began
to feel desperate. I could not wait, yet I dreaded the
dawn of the DAY. Suppose Lucienne Frécon was playing
a trick. No, no, Catherine had said in that infuriating
way of hers that she had known all about sugar-water
all along. Oh, the mean camel, I silently blasphemed,
not to have told me before. Sugar-water *must* be all right
then, since Catherine knew about it, too. All the same,
I went on praying very hard. . . .

"Happily we had something else unusual to occupy
our minds during those two endless days—the astonishing
behaviour of Mademoiselle Bobet. With two months'
holiday now in sight, Mademoiselle Bobet felt she
might unbend. So she unbent. She made little jokes,
she laughed, she asked friendly questions. One had an
uneasy feeling that with a little practice she might possibly
become like everybody else. It was most bewildering.
I don't know that I approved. I felt a teacher ought to
remain a teacher, or one didn't know where one was.

"Then suddenly it was Thursday. And there I was in my lovely frilly frock and my best buttoned boots that shone like the sun, as well they might after all the hours I'd spent on them with a piece of velvet left over from Catherine's new dress.

"Maman unfolded my sash and my heart stood still. She tied it; she untied it—very slowly, very carefully; one does not crease a sash like this. And at the third attempt, oh, miracle! My celestial sash encircled my waist with no hint of a pucker, a splendid satin butterfly spread its wings on my back, and two long ends rippled creaseless to the hem of my frock.

"Now for my hair. I did not sit down, of course. One did not crease one's frock until one had to. Catherine began to undo my forest of little plaits. I heard myself ask in a queer high voice, 'Is it all right?' I put up my hands to touch, and Catherine briskly smacked them with the comb. So I screwed up my eyes and prayed and prayed. 'Let it be all right. Let it be all right. Please! Please!' Then I heard Catherine say, 'Ça-y-est!' and she pushed me forward to look in the mirror.

"I saw my face very white, my eyes very dark and wide, and my hair, my beautiful, beautiful hair, very, very short, of course, but oh, so tightly, so delightfully frizzed all over my head! And surmounting it, my new hair-ribbon superbly tied. I must have looked like a prize little poodle-dog, of course, but to my enchanted eyes, I looked wonderful, most wonderful.

"Then I turned and kissed Maman and my darling clever sister Catherine, and with my head, neck and back all in one stiff piece so as not to rock my bows, I

166

half-walked, half-ran to school. And there were all the others in their best dresses and sashes, too, every head a frizzy masterpiece. And there were all the teachers in fine, unfamiliar dresses, and there was Mademoiselle Bobet, the most elegant of them all, in black silk with a gold watch pinned on her chest and a hat trimmed with Parma violets.

"We formed a procession, two by two, little ones in front, tallest bringing up the rear, and off we went: Rue de la Bourse, Place des Ursules, Cours Victor Hugo. Every now and then we politely slowed down or quickened our pace to oblige other processions of beautiful little girls with their elegant teachers. At the sight of them, I would put up my hand and delicately touch my hair. Then I would go on chattering, very lively, very confident, for my hair was behaving magnificently—it was still as bushy and crinkly as the mane of a little lion.

"And so we came to the Bourse du Travail with its majestic device: Liberty, Equality, Solidarity, Justice. We all poured into the Great Hall. An enormous hall, rows and rows of benches on the ground floor for us, and a gallery all round for our parents and friends. Facing us, a stage, as in a theatre if you please, with sumptuous red velvet curtains caught up on either side. On this stage a great table covered with a green cloth, and a number of lesser tables. On some of these were stacked the prizes—big books, little books, medium-sized books, but every book tied up with a lovely ribbon. On the other little tables were piles and piles of crowns. Yes, yes, crowns! Cardboard ones, but no one would have known, they looked absolutely real. Crowns of gold laurel leaves for the Prizes for Excellence, crowns of gold and green laurel leaves for the Prizes of Honour, crowns of green leaves studded with marguerites for all the other prizes.

"I looked and looked at all those books, all those crowns. Surely, surely, I would get a little book, a crown of leaves and marguerites . . . all those months of rigorous silence . . . not answering that Lucienne Frécon. Surely I could expect at least that. But one never knew with grown-ups. And there was also that arithmetic of mine. So I tried to concentrate on an enormous picture of a mine with the miners setting off for home. Then the Municipal Harmony came in. Very fine, our Municipal Harmony, in those days, I can tell you, with the arms of Saint Etienne embroidered in gold on their peaked caps. And no sooner had they settled down at the back of the stage than four grave gentlemen appeared and took up their places behind the large table. And Jacqueline Berthet by my side said that the gentleman, the one with the moustache like the picture of Vercingetorix in our history book, was Monsieur the Inspector who had come to our school the week I had my tonsils out. And the other one with the gold spectacles was Monsieur the Deputy-Mayor, and the one with the fine round stomach was Monsieur the Inspector of the Academy. Mademoiselle Bobet had just said so, and she ought to know. But, alas, I never learned what glorious function in life the fourth gentleman held, for at that moment the conductor of the Municipal Harmony brought down his baton with a resounding crack and we all rose to our feet to listen to the Marseillaise. Oh, Rouget de l'Isle would have been proud if he could only have heard our Municipal Harmony that day! And with our hearts very proud and warm, we all sat down and clapped and clapped.

"Then Monsieur the Deputy-Mayor stood up and began to speak.

"'The Municipality of Saint Etienne, conscious of its high duty, always striving to maintain with dignity and pride the traditions of honour of the Third Republic, ever upholding the generous principles of universal, laic, republican and obligatory education. . . .'

"And with more and more fine words he went on and on to speak of Paul Bert, Jules Ferry, Jean Macé and other unknown benefactors who had done so much for us sitting there . . . but what, I was not at all clear. From them he soared back to our glorious Revolution and by dramatic stages returned to give us much good advice, followed by warm words of praise for the municipality, our teachers, our parents, us, and everybody else in Saint Etienne. I considered this a very kind gesture; I wanted everybody, simply everybody, to feel happy on this great day. Then he flicked up the tails of his coat and, to tumultuous applause, sat down.

"And now up got Monsieur the Inspector of the Academy. But he told us funny stories and said we were not to mind too much if we did not get a prize and a crown this year—there was always next year. I began to think of next year. But no, my whole soul cried out that I could not endure another year of silence. Ah no! For me, it was this year or never. This year or NEVER!

"Then my heart began to thump, for the Distribution had begun. A voice was calling: 'School of the Place

Jacquard. Prize of Honour—Jeanne Fournier. Prize for Excellence—Louise Dumas.'

"Two little girls struggled out from the benches and climbed up to the stage. On one head went a crown of gold laurel leaves, on the other went a crown of gold and green. Monsieur the Deputy-Mayor handed them each a beribboned book and stooped to kiss them on both cheeks.

"But, strangely enough, I now began to feel that it might not be the end of all things if I did not receive a prize and a crown after all. Climb right up there, in front of all these girls . . . suppose my hair-ribbon fell off . . . suppose I stumbled and fell flat on my face . . . suppose my hair went suddenly straight . . . suppose my crown slipped over one ear and everybody laughed. In vain did I watch other little girls return to their seats, safely crowned and bearing their prizes. I saw only the dark disasters that might befall *me*, Françoise Lombard. These other little girls were perhaps different; they were perhaps used to being kissed by Deputy-Mayors, used to walking across a stage, used to wearing crowns.

"Then somebody gave me a sharp nudge. A voice was calling: 'School of the Place Bert'—*my* school. 'Prize of Honour—Josephine Garnier. Prize for Excellence—Françoise Lombard.'

"Françoise Lombard. Me. But I'd heard wrong, of course. I was dreaming, of course. Dreaming.

" 'Go on,' hissed a million voices, 'it's you! Go on! Hurry up!'

"I got up. I walked kilometres and kilometres down the hall. I climbed a towering flight of five steps. I was pushed towards Monsieur the Inspector. He set a crown on my head, a crown of gold laurel leaves. Monsieur the Deputy-Mayor offered me a book, a beautiful red book tied up with a lovely pink ribbon. He said something about perseverance and industry, and stooped to kiss me on both my crimson cheeks.

"And then, there I was back in my seat! But how I had arrived there I simply did not know. And all about me, the little girls were saying, 'What is it? Come on, let us look. Oh, it isn't a story! What a shame! What a nasty shame!'

"So I looked at my prize, too. It was a *History of the Glorious French Revolution*. But the ribbon tied round it was magnificent and I decided not to untie it till I got home. Perhaps there were pictures inside as well as history.

"Somehow, now, I did not feel at all interested in all the other prize-winners still going up to be crowned and kissed. I tried to see if I could spot Maman and Catherine up in the gallery. Then I kindly helped other little girls to spot their relations, too. And all the while the noise was growing and growing. Nobody, not even the Deputy-Mayor, could expect a whole hall full of little girls to remain quiet all this time. The four gentlemen on the stage, therefore, decided to accelerate the Distribution. Crowns, prizes, kisses were all speeded up, and soon not a crown, not a prize was left. The noise had gathered up momentum, too, and Monsieur the Inspector had to shout his last words. But we heard them, oh yes, we heard them: 'Happy holidays, children!'

"At this, the Municipal Harmony struck up a lively

march, the four gentlemen climbed down from the stage and began to shake hands right and left, and we all began to talk at the tops of our voices. I remember thinking for one fleeting moment what a pity it was that nobody could hear the Municipal Harmony playing vigorously away, before I, too, joined in the din, the joyous struggle towards the door.

"I had to find Maman and Catherine. They must be the first to admire my prize and my crown. Then I'd be off on my round of visits. That was traditional. Every prize-winner visited every soul the family knew. First I would call on Tante Virginie, then my godmother, then Madame Brossard who had starched my frock, then this one, and that one. . . . Oh yes, I had my list most carefully prepared. They would all admire my crown, my prize, my dress, my sash, and my hair—my lovely hair still frizzing so faithfully all over my head. They would offer me a little refreshment, of course, and finally they would present me with something for my money-box. Grandmother would come down handsomely. So would Tante Virginie. The others might well be generous, too. I had the Prize for Excellence, hadn't I?

"Oh, the rest of the day was going to be wonderful, a blaze of glory.

"And after that, well, after that there would be the holidays, two long months of brand-new days.

"I tell you, I had never known such shining happiness, never, never."

Françoise was silent for a moment.

"And I will tell you something else," she said presently. "Last year I scraped together enough to pay for

a 'permanent' from that inspired triple brigand, Anatole
—Coiffeur de Dames.

"And he held up his mirror, and sighed, 'Mademoiselle
will admit that I have surpassed even myself.'

"And it was true. There was this thin hair of mine
curling most casually all over my head, absolutely
Madame le Brun.

"And suddenly I wanted to cry. Not at the sight of my
expensive new elegance. No, no, I had caught for a
moment, for one little moment, the lovely delight of that
shining day—the day of my Distribution of Prizes."

Françoise gave a sigh.

And suddenly there we were again, sitting outside a
café on the Place Marengo.

It was a little chilly now, and very dark. The brass
band had packed up and gone home.

But there, under the quiet trees, it seemed to me I could
still see the little girl who was my cousin Françoise,
flying across the square, bow of ribbon dancing on her
dark head, satin sash streaming behind her as she ran.

Maybe Françoise and Catherine saw her as well. For
they were strangely silent, too.

12

The Friends of the Pedal go Sight-Seeing

The days sped by, but still there was no sign of my suitcase, no word from Monsieur Durand. I felt more and more puzzled, and hurt. But I could not bring myself to write again. Nor did I say anything of what I felt to my cousins.

Happily we were far too busy making the most of our holiday to have much time for solitary thought. Françoise positively revelled in telling me family stories to which I listened entranced, of course. But Catherine, too, was full of surprises. She was not only widely read, she had a store of solid knowledge that amazed me.

And she saw to it that I gathered the soundest of impressions, especially of all that concerned Saint Etienne.

This is why I know so much about a certain literary nobleman who one summer day in the year 1607 sat at a window of his château not many miles from Saint Etienne and looked long and lovingly over the green and pleasant countryside.

Then he dipped his quill pen into his handsome silver inkstand and began the first paragraph of the first chapter of the first volume of a brand-new romance—a long rambling tale of love and friendship and the gentler pleasures of country life.

It was all so refined, so idyllic, that when volume one appeared, the critics up in Paris sneered that the noble writer cooed like the chastest of doves in the most genteel of woods.

But humbler readers all over France were swift to see the queer moving sincerity running all through those cooing polished periods. And weary of the brutality of long and senseless wars, weary of the coarse obscenity of the writers of the day, they eagerly lapped up the new romance, all five volumes of it—much to the rage of the critics up in Paris, who even in those days had no patience whatever with the deplorable longing of ordinary folk to be taken out of themselves and into a more kindly, flower-strewn world of make-believe.

But the ribbon-makers, the pottery-makers, the carpet-makers were swift to recognise a good theme when they read one, and enthusiastically set to work turning out ribbons, vases and carpets pictured with rural scenes from the new novel. All of which also sold like hot cakes, not only in France but all over Europe as well; so that Céladon the shepherd, the hero of the novel, dallied affectionately, but most virtuously, with Astrée his shepherdess-love, on vases, plates, cushions, and rugs, in well-appointed drawing-rooms everywhere from Moscow to Versailles.

The literary nobleman who wrote this best-seller was Honoré d'Urfé; his romance was called *L'Astrée*, and he took eighteen long years to write it.

Nobody nowadays reads all five volumes of *L'Astrée*. They haven't the time—not even in Saint Etienne. But this does not mean that people there have forgotten their illustrious author. On the contrary. The largest girls' school in Saint Etienne, for instance, is still proud to be called the Lycée d'Honoré d'Urfé.

All this I learned one day when Catherine and I were passing this school and I light-heartedly asked who Honoré d'Urfé might be when he was at home.

I was not only told, in great detail, but Catherine, scandalised, cried, "And you stand there and tell me you have never heard of him! And you a teacher, too! What about Corneille, Racine and La Fontaine? Are you now going to tell me no British teacher has ever heard about them either?"

I cautiously admitted that these names sounded rather more familiar, and was told that these literary gentlemen had dipped with both hands into the treasures of *L'Astrée*.

"With no acknowledgments whatever, of course," said Catherine.

"Furthermore," went on my well-informed cousin, "all worthwhile writers on the country around Saint Etienne still quote our Honoré d'Urfé." And she took my arm and marched me straight into the nearest book-shop to prove it.

Sure enough, the first guide-book we opened said:

"Tourists, my brothers! Welcome to Saint Etienne!

"Tourists, my brothers, pause to consider all Saint Etienne can offer you!

"By admirable roads from our city centre you may discover for yourself our enchanting countryside of Forez, of which the oldest description is still the truest:

" 'Forez in its smallness holds all that is rarest in the

rest of Gaul. It is divided into plain and mountain, and everywhere the air is so temperate, the soil so fertile, that it is capable of producing everything the honest labourer desires.

" 'In the heart of this countryside is the most beautiful plain encircled by lofty mountain peaks. Close by is the source of the River Loire; and this river flows across our plain, not swollen and arrogant, but most gentle and peaceful.'

"Tourists, my brothers, these are the immortal words of Honoré d'Urfé; first paragraph, first chapter, first volume of his delightful romance, *L'Astrée*."

"There!" said Catherine triumphantly, and closed and replaced the book. "Heavens, no, we needn't buy it! A couple of postcards will do."

Now Honoré d'Urfé may have written the most fancy stuff and nonsense about shepherds and shepherdesses, but when he sang the praises of the countryside about Saint Etienne he wrote straight from the heart. It *is* enchanting.

Every week-end, we Friends of the Pedal would set out on the admirable roads bound for villages with the most entrancing of names: Valfleury, Apple Trees of Forez, Saint-Julien-Molin-Molette, Saint Régis-of-the-Corner, and many others, but all with names that sounded to me like the first line of an old poem.

And many of them look the part; they have a quaint ancient loveliness unchanged by time—the village of Saint-Croise-en-Jarez, for instance, still lies within the walls of a medieval monastery.

But Françoise, of course, would listen to the more poetical Friends of the Pedal raving about all this, and then roundly declare that poems were all right out here in the country, but she herself preferred drains to poetry any day of the week.

Then I was taken on what Catherine called "cycling pilgrimages" to places she felt a teacher like me ought to see—the Bâtie d'Urfé, for instance, a lovely old manor-house, set in the greenest and most gracious of country. No wonder I thought that Honoré d'Urfé, just back from the wars, looked so gratefully from its windows, and contentedly spent eighteen delightful years writing about gentle shepherds and shepherdesses walking under those great trees, reclining on the banks of that quiet river, in their very best clothes, never dirtying their white hands; but talking poetically about enough true love and gallantry to fill five great volumes.

And very peculiar and awkward I felt at first, I can tell you, wobbling away in the rear of these expeditions. I never thought anyone would ever talk me into a pair of slacks—and pale blue ones at that, a pair of Catherine's that had`considerably shrunk to just my length of leg. And Françoise energetically talking and buttoning me into them, announced that she had the very "puhl" to complete my cycling outfit; and when I said, "What on earth's a 'puhl'?" she said, "Heavens above, the woman is forgetting her own language!" And brought out the "puhl"—a pullover, a tooth-paste pink one with cyclists in blue cross-stitch racing across the chest and down each sleeve.

Then every Wednesday evening the Friends of the Pedal would crowd into our little living-room and make plans for our next outing over a bottle of wine and a cup of coffee. And I began to notice that a quiet unobtrusive little gentleman called Monsieur Benoit Frécon always lingered for a while after all the others had found their hats, shaken hands and gone home. He was a very old friend, I gathered, and a white-hot cyclist, always talking brakes, gears and hubs. In fact I had the impression that he just lived for cycling and his business—a busy little stationer's shop, "maps for cyclists a speciality"—in the centre of the town.

One Sunday, however, we went for another of our "cycling pilgrimages", this time to pay our respectful homage and to eat our picnic-lunch at the foot of a monument erected by the side of a road that led through a great forest of fir trees, a monument to the memory of a Monsieur Paul de Vivie, "apostle of the polymultiple cycle and of cycle-tourism".

We were cycling down the long hill to Saint Etienne again, when Monsieur Frécon slowed down and began to ride by my side.

"This cycling," he said. "You like it, Miss Dor-o-tee?"

I said, well, yes, I did, now I had got used to my pedals . . . and my pale-blue slacks.

He wheeled still nearer, leaned over, and hissed in my ear, "Please, not a word, above all to your cousins, but confidentially, most confidentially, me, I detest it. I DETEST it!"

I nearly fell off, I was so staggered. And Monsieur Frécon, very gratified at my surprise, said darkly, "But

I have my reasons. Oh yes, Miss Dor-o-tee, believe me, I have very grave reasons."

I thought he was delicately hinting that cycling was good for his liver, so I gave an understanding "Ah!" and we rode on in sympathetic silence.

The following Sunday, however, we did not go out with the Friends of the Pedal. We had been invited to spend the day in a village called Saint Bonnet-by-the-River, to see something they called the "Vogue", the annual feast-day, I gathered. The invitation had come from an old school-friend of Catherine's, Ernestine Dupont. She was the schoolmistress there.

So on that Sunday, and not in our slacks, we took the early morning bus to Saint Bonnet-on-the-River.

It was a pretty little village set in a valley: church, post office, school, cafés and shops, all set about a shady market-square, and all gaily decorated for the Vogue with paper-chains, flags, and green branches stuck with gaudy paper flowers.

We went straight over to a trim little house by the side of the school, and out ran Ernestine and made us most welcome. We were in excellent time, she said. High Mass would be over any minute now, Monsieur le Curé being a reasonable priest who always cut his sermon short on a Vogue Day. And she brought out four chairs and set them in a row on the pavement outside and invited us to sit down.

Almost immediately the bells began to ring, the church doors were flung open, and out poured the people, led by a dozen or so excited young men wearing wide straw hats trimmed with red or green ribbons.

"Now those lads," said Ernestine, "are known as the Voguers. They arrange everything. They've been going round for weeks past collecting funds for today. Ah, look, here come the firemen!"

And now out from the church marched a brass band, helmets on their heads gleaming like gold in the sun.

"Oh yes," said Ernestine proudly, "they are our firemen. But we don't get many fires, and when we do get one, there's plenty of water in the river, so they fill in their evenings with a little music. We're not like some villages round here who have to pay good money for one of these jazz bands to come out from Lyons or Saint Etienne."

As she spoke a grand procession was forming up before the church, the firemen's brass band in front, the Voguers behind, the first two carrying a great laundry-basket, tastefully decorated with paper flowers. As they marched past us, I saw that this basket was piled high with "brioches"—a kind of rich, flaky bun. And behind them, of course, pranced every child in the village.

With the drum beating, and all four trumpets sounding, the procession marched three times round the market-square, came to a resounding halt outside the presbytery, and set down the laundry-basket. Out came Monsieur le Curé and waited expectantly whilst the Voguers took a plate from the basket, set a fine white serviette on it, placed a brioche in the exact centre, and politely offered it to him. As he graciously accepted it, the band struck up a tune called, "Oh, Warm Sun of Provence", and Monsieur le Curé, brioche in hand, stood there, listening, face shining with pleasure.

Then off went the procession again, and this time came to a halt outside the mayor's house—every village in France has its mayor. And out he marched, red, white and blue sash about his portly waist, and accepted a brioche in the name of the Republic; and we all rose to our feet as the band tackled the Marseillaise.

Then off they went once more, this time straight towards the post office.

"Ah!" said Ernestine. "Now this is going to be interesting. Our postmaster is a red-hot Communist." But out stalked Comrade Postmaster, accepted his brioche with gentlemanly dignity, and stood, brioche in one fist, the other clenched and raised in salute as the band did their best with "The People's Flag is Deepest Red".

"Well! Well!" murmured Ernestine. "Altogether Papa Stalin! But he has his rights, of course. Everyone who pays something towards the Vogue can call for their own tune."

But now the procession was heading straight for us, so we hastily got to our feet, and as Ernestine received her brioche the band gave a mighty poum-poum-poum and struggled valiantly with something that sounded vaguely familiar.

"Well," said Françoise, very touched. "Isn't that charming? Ernestine must have told them you were coming, Dor-o-tee!"

So I listened intently. And yes, it was. It was "God Save the King". Definitely "God Save the King".

Then away went the procession again to offer a brioche and play a request-number at every house in the village. And we went in to lunch.

And with us went a dozen more people whom Ernestine had also invited; and how she managed to get us seated round her table, I cannot explain. But there we were, jammed merrily side by side, talking away to everyone else to right and to left and across the table.

And what a meal! We began just after twelve with slices of sausage and ham. Then came delicious pastry affairs, light as air, and filled with mushrooms, olives, and tomatoes. This was followed by a great dish of young runner-beans, after which we tackled roast chicken flanked with a mountain of salad. Then came the cheese, and after that a massive cherry tart. All of which we washed down with three sorts of light sparkling wine.

At three o'clock we pushed back our plates; Ernestine brought in the coffee; and the gentlemen were persuaded to give us a song or two, the good old songs such as "Halt, halt, the Mountain Troops are Here!" and one that went:

"No, dear comrade," he said, as he sank in the foam,
"You take the life-belt, you have two children at home."

Then we all joined in a ballad that ran:

This crystal goblet, rare and fine,
Is not worth the humble glass
In which I drank 'neath yonder vine
In days now fled, alas!
Today I sit and drink alone
But as I drink I see
The golden days that I have known,
The friends so dear to me.

183

We all quickly cheered up, however, when Ernestine passed round little glasses of a very special liqueur made from the plums that ripened on the walls of the school, and which everyone declared was the most delicious and potent of digestives; in fact one gentleman swore he preferred it to "La Grande Chartreuse" itself.

Then another gentleman rose to his feet and in a warm rolling Provençal accent gave us "Ma Normandie". I confided in Françoise sitting by my side that this sounded rather like a Welsh tenor yearning for his bonny, bonny Banks of Loch Lomond. And she said, well, what about the First World War, and those brave Tommies of ours from London who sang incessantly about this Tipperary over in Ireland. Names didn't matter. Home was where the heart was. And very moved, we both finished up our liqueur and listened to the last verse:

> *There comes a time in every life*
> *When every dream fades, faint and cold,*
> *And when the heart so worn with strife*
> *Recalls once more dear scenes of old.*
> *And when all this must come to me,*
> *As come it must, it is Life's way,*
> *Please God, I'll go to Normandy,*
> *Where first my eyes beheld the day.*

We liked this verse so much that we sang it all over again, with the greatest feeling. And then a distant poum-poum-poum brought us all to our feet, and we streamed out to see the procession again.

Now, every Voguer had a smiling girl on his arm, flowers in her hair, bouquet in her hand. Ernestine said they were making another tour of the village, stopping every now and then for a little refreshment, of course, till it was time to lead off the Grand Ball on the market-square that evening.

"But, just a minute!" she exclaimed, and pointed to a solitary figure sitting outside a café on the other side of the square. "Isn't that a friend of yours?"

And when we looked, why, there, bicycle leaning against his chair, drooped Monsieur Benoit Frécon!

"No!" said Catherine. "Can't be! I refuse to believe my eyes. He *never* misses his Sunday ride with the club, never!"

"Well, he has today," said Ernestine. "Do bring the poor gentleman over!"

But before we had time to raise a shout, Monsieur Frécon grabbed his cycle, jumped on, and was off round the corner, without one backward glance, as fast as his pedals would carry him.

"Pécaïre!" cried Catherine. "The man's mad!"

"No, no, suddenly shy," said kind Ernestine. "I have a brother like that. Runs like a hare rather than shake hands with a lot of strangers. But what about bringing the chairs out here now, so that we can see everybody and everything?"

So we brought out all the chairs; and all that long sunny afternoon there we sat, merrily cluttering up the pavement, listening to the brass band, and chatting with the neighbours, who all exclaimed what a pity, what a thousand pities it was that the last bus to Saint Etienne went back so early—we would miss the Grand Ball and so much of the fun.

Then, as Ernestine absolutely insisted on another festive snack before we left, we caught this last bus by the very skin of our teeth; and we leaned out of the window, panting, to catch a last glimpse of Saint Bonnet-by-the-River, all lit up with strings of fairy lights, fire-works blazing, brass band still going strong, not to mention the organ on a little roundabout that had just been set up in front of the post office and which two perspiring Voguers were now working by hand.

As the bus rounded a great bend in the road the music and lights died behind us. And Catherine grabbed my arm.

"Look!" she gasped. "Look!"

And there, pedalling grimly away behind our bus, very pale and determined, was Monsieur Benoit Frécon!

As we stared, the bus suddenly gathered up speed and shot ahead, and the darkness swallowed him up.

So when we got out at Saint Etienne, we naturally hung about for a while waiting for him to turn up. "He *must* have something on his mind," said Catherine, very worried. "About the club, maybe."

"Then it will have to wait," said Françoise presently. "We can't wait here all night."

And we set off for home, still wondering what on earth had come over him.

13

Two Letters Arrive

The next morning, however, we had something far more astonishing to discuss.

To begin with, I had two letters; a thick one with an English stamp, and a thin one with a French stamp.

I opened the English one first. As I thought, it was from Miss Clarkson of the modern school. She began by thanking me for all my interesting postcards which she had pinned upon the noticeboard in the hall. Then she rather acidly said that she had wanted to write to me long before this, but I omitted to give her any address. Moreover, my last card, which *did* give my cousins' address, had arrived when the school was closed for the Whitsuntide holidays; and Mr. Lazenby, the caretaker, had not seen fit once again to forward any correspondence except one absurd advertisement for somebody's soap which was marked "Urgent! Open at once! This means money to you!"

And this really had been most annoying, as Miss Clarkson had been to the International Conference of a famous club for women in which she took an active part—as a delegate for the district she was pleased to say. There she had met the American delegate from New

York, an elderly but lively lady, and a great traveller, called Mrs. Luvisa Van Winkle. And Miss Clarkson had faithfully promised this lady to write to me immediately to see if I would help her to get into touch with a French-woman who would like a job as her companion; not a young person but a middle-aged woman, in good health, of course, friendly, practical, clever with her needle, and, above all, fond of travelling, as Mrs. Van Winkle was now planning to do Italy, Egypt and Australia before returning to New York.

In short, this person would have to be prepared to be away at least two years before returning, with Mrs. Van Winkle, to France, where she was then considering settling down, near Cannes probably.

And Miss Clarkson had assured Mrs. Van Winkle that I was just the person to help her; being right on the spot, I would gladly find out the address of a good agency, or put an advertisement in some sober provincial paper. However, now, in view of all this regrettable delay, Miss Clarkson wondered if my cousins or any of their friends knew of a suitable person in whom Mrs. Van Winkle could have every confidence. The wages, by the way, would be good. So, if I could help, would I get into touch with Mrs. Van Winkle *immediately*, in Paris, where she was now staying. And Miss Clarkson underlined "immediately" three times, and gave me Mrs. Van Winkle's Paris telephone number: Odeon something or the other.

Miss Clarkson then began another urgent paragraph, in which she told me she was, of course, absolutely worked off her feet, and hinted that it was high time I gave some indication of when I proposed to return and lend a hand, next term she hoped; and with good wishes from herself and all the staff, she was mine sincerely, Cecilia Clarkson.

I translated every word of this to my interested cousins, of course.

"Ah no! These globe-trotting Americans!" laughed Françoise. "Not my idea of enjoying myself!"

"But think of it," said Catherine. "Italy . . . Egypt . . . New York!"

There was something so strange in her voice that we both turned to look at her.

"Why, Catherine," cried Françoise, "I do believe. . ."

"Nonsense!" said Catherine. "No, no, of course not. Don't be ridiculous. It's not to be thought of!"

"And why not?" said Françoise, suddenly very quiet. "I can remember the time when you used to say you would give anything to travel, to get out of Saint Etienne, and see the world."

"I still would," said Catherine. "But how could I . . ."

"Listen, if you are thinking of me . . . No, no, don't interrupt! I will tell Dor-o-tee everything."

Then Françoise told me that for some years now they had realised that one day they would have to give up their ribbon-making. They had never discussed it openly when their father was alive; he was one of the old generation who passionately believed in sticking to one's trade, good days and evil. But there were now far too many weeks in which they earned far too little, and it looked as if things would never be better, not in our time, anyway.

After all, ribbons were luxuries, especially their sort of ribbon. Women simply could not afford them.

So they were considering buying a small business. To tell the truth, that was why they had decided to have this holiday—to look round, as it were. They hadn't told me before because they didn't want me to feel in the way; oh no, they weren't going to risk that. Besides, there was plenty of time. They had a little put away, Papa had always insisted on that. And Monsieur Frécon, who had an excellent head when it came to business, he was looking round for them, too.

"Té!" said Catherine. "Maybe that is why he wanted to see us on Sunday!"

"Well, he must have thought better of it," said Françoise; and she leaned across the table and took my hand.

"Dor-o-tee," she said, "I know we can ask you to tell us the truth, the simple truth. Do you think that our Catherine here is the kind of companion this American lady requires?"

"No, I'm not," said Catherine abruptly. "I am ordinary, far too ordinary. You must see that."

"I think Mrs. Van Winkle would be a very fortunate woman to find someone like Catherine," I said, and I meant it every word.

"Ah!" said Françoise, very satisfied.

"Oh, talk sense!" implored Catherine.

"I will," said Françoise. "I think you should ring up this American lady, that you should go to Paris if necessary. You can at least see if she likes you, if you like her."

"But, Françoise . . ." stuttered Catherine.

"No, no," said Françoise. "I am not having it on my tender conscience that a sister of mine turned her back on the chance of going half round the world, and getting paid for it, too! Nothing may come of it. But at least you can telephone, ask if she is still looking for someone. We can argue afterwards. What was that telephone number, Dor-o-tee?"

And still talking hard, she fairly hustled Catherine out of the house, ordering her to telephone Mrs. Van Winkle from the nearest post office.

Then she turned to me. "My poor Dor-o-tee," she cried, "with all this, you haven't opened your other letter yet." And she sat down, and waited for the next surprise.

So I opened the other letter; and yes, it *was* from Monsieur Durand. Very formal. Very polite. He sent a thousand apologies for taking so long to reply to my welcome letter, and said this brief scrawl was to let me know that he would be in Lyons that very day on important business and would take the opportunity to bring my suitcase with him. So would I meet him at the Café Lyonnais opposite the main entrance to the Perrache Station there between ten and eleven.

"Between ten and eleven today!" I said, and looked at the clock. "Well, I like that. The very idea, giving me so little notice! I can't do it, of course. I just won't be able to get there in time."

And I don't think I have ever felt so put out, so hurt.

"But you can!" screamed Françoise. "You can! Come on! Powder your nose. I'll get out your 'trotter'!"

"My what?" I asked.

"Your grey 'trotter'," said Françoise exasperated. And she got out the "trotter"—my grey tweed costume, hustled me into it, slapped a hat on my head, handed me my bag; and I just had time to grab gloves and guide-book before she ran me out of the house as well.

And before I had time to think, there I was sitting in the train, heading for Lyons.

Now the journey from Saint Etienne to Lyons takes about an hour. And when I'd straightened my hat, and got my breath back again, I closed my eyes, leaned back, and tried to do some clear thinking. I told myself that Miss Clarkson was right; it was indeed high time I considered when I proposed to return. I would have to go back to the modern school, of course. What else was there to do? My money wouldn't last much longer.

And it was high time I began to take this long holiday of mine more seriously too.

"For instance," I said to myself, "you won't be long getting your suitcase from Monsieur Durand. He'll probably have to rush straight off to see about this important business of his. So you get down to some intelligent sight-seeing for once. You have a look at that expensive guide-book of yours; you've hardly opened it since you came to France. You get ready to tell Form 1C all about Lyons in the long years to come."

So I opened my guide-book, found a nail-file in my bag, and cut the first two pages about Lyons.

The Place Bellecour, I read, was the finest city square in all Europe. Napoleon himself had seen to that. There was a remarkable equestrian statue of Louis XIV. . . .

But try as I might, I could not concentrate on the Place Bellecour or on the statue of Louis XIV.

I thought of Catherine, her eyes dark and wide, as she said, "Italy . . . Egypt . . . New York!"

I wondered if she would go to Paris to see Mrs. Van Winkle, if she would go off travelling with her half round the world.

If so, what would Françoise do? Perhaps she would come back to England with me. But no, I couldn't see Françoise settling down in England; her heart was in Saint Etienne. Maybe I could persuade her to come for a long holiday. And after that. . . . Well, after that seemed so bleak, so empty, that I was quite glad when the train steamed into Lyons. But for the life of me, I could not understand why I felt so nervous. All the rush and excitement, I supposed.

When I walked out of the station, there, just across the road, sitting outside a café, was Monsieur Durand, looking extremely smart in a new brown tweed suit, yellow tie with red spots, a very wide felt hat—a biscuit-coloured one, and very shiny new yellow shoes.

As I crossed over to him, he shot to his feet and swept off his hat. "Miss," he said. "I am very 'appy. How are you? Please sit down. I was commencing to think perhaps you are not coming."

"Why!" I thought. "He's nervous, too!" Oddly enough, that made me feel better. And we shook hands and sat down, and he ordered something for us both. Then he threw up both hands in a comic gesture of despair. "Bouffre!" he said. "All these days and days I am saying I must tell Miss this, and that, also this. But now I am seeing you, what happens? I find no English. I have the tongue all in wood."

This made us both laugh. And I asked how little Pierre was. "I will tell you," he said solemnly. "I will tell you the simple truth. He has made a lamentable discovery. He now refuses to believe I am the most wonderful Papa in France. I have, alas, no stories at all about remarkable rabbits!"

Then he went on to tell me that he had planned to bring my suitcase up to Lyons weeks ago, no sense spending good money sending it by rail; besides, he *had* to come on this business of his, anyway. But he simply had not been able to arrange a day off. Angélique! Yes, Angélique was the reason for the delay. She had been having the very devil of a time with her young man from Marseilles. No, no, it wasn't that he was still so jealous, so suspicious! It was that all of a sudden he was not jealous any more! And poor Angélique, smelling a very peculiar rat, had made her little investigations. And found her Placide in the most expensive café in all Nîmes, gazing into the great brown eyes of a costly blonde— and all on the cash he had borrowed from Angélique if I pleased!

But Angélique had shown her! She had come home victorious all right, supported by two sympathetic policemen. And then there had been other complications, legal as well as emotional. And as I knew, she was a good straight girl, Angélique, and very conscientious, especially about little Pierre. Girls like Angélique did not grow on every tree. So he had waited for things to sort themselves out. But, of course, he had not felt able to leave her in charge, no, not even for a single day. But now, thank God, she was over the worst. She was almost her old, sensible self again. And well, here he was!

As for my friends, the regulars, they weren't great shakes at letter-writing either; but every evening they spoke of me, wondered how I was getting on, hoped I was happy with my new family. And they all sent a thousand friendly greetings and looked forward with the warmest pleasure to seeing me again and hearing all my news.

As I listened to all this, I felt very humble, very ashamed. How could I have doubted such friends? But I didn't say so, of course. On the contrary, I began to say that it was a real pleasure to have seen him again but that I simply must not detain him. I knew he had important business to attend to, and I myself felt I ought to see something of Lyons now I was there.

And, by the way, where was my suitcase?

"Oh, that!" said Monsieur Durand airily. "I have put it in the cloakroom over there in the station. You will not want to carry it about all day. As for Lyons, well, I can tell you all about Lyons. They make silks here. And velvets. And spaghetti, very nice spaghetti, all shapes and sizes. And the citizens are all stiff and silent. They also have fogs, yes, fogs as in London."

He called to the waiter, ordered some more refreshment and said, "It is true, what I am telling this lady, eh, that you have fogs here in Lyons?"

The waiter, with melancholy pride, said Monsieur was right. They had fogs. Oh, not maybe as in London where they were classed as pea-soupers. But after London,

Lyons was definitely considered to hold the championship in fogs. The European championship, of course. Perhaps in America even the fogs were bigger and thicker than anywhere else as well.

And he gave us a wintry smile and went off to get the drinks.

I said perhaps a strapping young Yank had run off with his girl. But Monsieur Durand said, no, all these Lyonnais were like that, very bleak but truthful. And no wonder either, when one considered their fogs.

"I tell you," said Monsieur Durand, "I was here one day last winter and I could not see my own feet walking along. It was a very nasty feeling, just like walking in a world of cotton wool.

"And then I was aware of a dull clop-clop-clop very near me. I stopped. It stopped. I took a few more steps. And again I heard it. Clop-clop-clop. Very near. Far too near.

"'Ah!' I thought. 'An assassin! Any moment now, and I shall feel a gun in my back. A voice will demand my wallet and my watch. But I will show him! I will teach him to rob a Provençal gentleman lost in a fog!'

"And I stopped again, ready to fight for my life. And this is not amusing, not at my age.

"But suddenly I began to laugh! Yes, I laughed till I wept.

"This sinister clop-clop-clop, it was me! Yes, me! Those were my feet down there, lost in the fog, going clop-clop-clop!

"And I will tell you something else," said Monsieur Durand. "Do you know what they are selling in all the little kiosks along their quays? Onion soup! Good strong onion soup, so that poor devils can follow their noses safely to it, and not walk, flack, right into one of their two cold rivers.

"And that," said Monsieur Durand, "is all there is to know about Lyons."

"Now, now," I said. "I know better than that. There is this Place Bellecour, for instance, the finest city square in all Europe. I really ought to go and have a look at that."

Monsieur Durand said Place Bellecour, come to think of it, he had been to Lyons dozens of times, but he had never seen this Place Bellecour either. So he would come with me.

And he paid the waiter and off we went.

But when we came to the Place Bellecour not an inch of the finest city square in all Europe could we see. There were hoardings all round it, very high wooden hoardings.

"Ah, but look up there!" said Monsieur Durand. "Nobody can keep that gentleman down!"

And there, high in the trees, staring haughtily over the hoardings, we could just see the head of Louis XIV.

"Here!" said Monsieur Durand to a waiter hovering outside a nearby restaurant. "What is the meaning of this? This lady comes all the way from England to see your Place Bellecour. And what does she see? This . . . this concentration camp! Why, it is enough to make our Napoleon turn in his grave!"

The waiter turned a chilly blue eye on him. "Monsieur

is then not aware that the final of the Grand National Competition of Bowls is being held here today?"

"National Competition of Bowls, eh?" said Monsieur Durand, suddenly very interested. "Then you'll be putting on a special menu, of course?"

"But certainly, Monsieur," said the waiter and held out a large, closely printed document.

"Mm," said Monsieur Durand, studying it. "Not bad. Not bad. Yes, I think we may as well eat here, before all these bowlers rush out and finish up everything."

So we sat down at one of the tables on the wide pavement, and Monsieur Durand ordered a meal, a wonderful meal I thought, but Monsieur Durand wasn't handing out unnecessary compliments. And it tickled me to see how the waiter hovered about him, very deferential now, very anxious to please this jovial gentleman from Provence who was obviously on more than nodding terms with all the exclusive and most expensive "specialités"—even their famous "Spring Chicken in Half-Mourning".

"No, not bad, not bad at all," admitted Monsieur Durand, helping himself liberally to potatoes, sliced and fried a delicate brown with a sprinkling of crisp chopped onion. "But they are too enthusiastic with their onions up here. Now we, in Provence, we prefer a shade more garlic."

I said I'd noticed that; and he said that one also had to admit that these Lyonnais knew a thing or two about wine. This Beaujolais we were drinking, for instance, was quite bright and cheerful in its way. And, by heaven, they needed cheering up. Standoffish lot, the people here;

got to know one just in time to accept an invitation to one's funeral.

At that moment the gentlemen playing in the bowls competition came pouring out from the Place Bellecour and sat down on every chair, briskly arguing and bandying obscure jokes that I gathered only other bowlers could truly appreciate. But not when deciding on their meal, however. Over that, they held long, solemn consultation with the waiter.

"And quite right, too," approved Monsieur Durand. "A game is one thing, a meal is another. Every sensible man takes his food seriously."

Then I happened to mention that over in England bowlers played on the finest of grass, lovely lawns as smooth and even as velvet.

And Monsieur Durand threw up both hands, and cried, heavens above, French bowlers knew better than to demand high-sport amenities like that. Any handy piece of hard ground did them, as long as it was reasonably flat.

Then the bowlers called for their bills, paid up, and went off to get on with the competition. But we still sat on, talking of this and that.

Presently, however, I said that maybe it was time I started on a little sight-seeing; and Monsieur Durand immediately said, oh yes, we really ought to do a little digestive footing. And he called to the respectful waiter, paid him, and off we went.

But which way we went, I cannot say. All I know is that we strolled on and on, along many a pleasant shady street, till we came to the place where the two rivers of

Lyons meet: the Saône very slow and green, the Rhône swift and grey. And there we stood, gazing at it.

"A very sensible marriage, that," observed Monsieur Durand. "Together they make a fine steady river."

It was then that I looked at my watch and gasped. It was a quarter to five, and I had promised to catch the five o'clock train back to Saint Etienne. Françoise was coming to the station to meet me.

So Monsieur Durand hailed a passing taxi, instructed the driver to go like the wind, and in we got.

But now a strange silence fell between us. With hardly another word we tore from the taxi to the station cloak-room, got out my suitcase, and raced down the platform. The train was in, and behind us the ticket-collector was shouting because Monsieur Durand had rushed past without a platform ticket. I climbed in; he handed up my suitcase; we shook hands; I tried to thank him for a lovely day; and the train began to move out.

Suddenly I felt hot and then cold.

"Oh, Monsieur Durand!" I cried. "Your business! The business that brought you to Lyons! I do hope I've not made you too late!"

"No! No! I assure you!" he panted, running alongside the train.

"You see, Miss . . . my dear Miss . . . this business . . . it was you!"

14

Catherine Meets Mrs. Van Winkle

The train was more than full, and all the way home I sat on my suitcase in the corridor, my thoughts boiling away in strangest confusion.

I told myself not to be a fool. Monsieur Durand was, of course, just being extra polite. He was that sort of man, most warmly impulsive.

I reminded myself how Angélique, who delighted to give me the benefit of her wide experience, had once wound up her instalment for the day with, "No, no, Miss, I tell you there's no banking on any man. Take Monsieur Durand here. Now he's good, I'll say that, as good as bread, but a real saucepan of milk, up in a flash! And as I said, he's good, a boss in a million in fact."

Well, I'd had a day in a million, a golden day.

I hadn't seen any of the sights, of course. I hadn't even bought my usual, conscience-salving batch of picture postcards.

And I saw myself again stepping out of the train that morning, positively garlanded with earnest resolutions to "do" Lyons in the future interests of Form 1C.

Well, anybody with a guide book could "do" Lyons.

But nobody could ever see Lyons as I now saw it, as I should always see it—wrapped in a genial champion of a fog, turning out velvet, silk, spaghetti of all sizes and shapes, and good onion soup for the fogbound.

Oh, a golden city, Lyons, where important business had once waited on me, Dorothy Durand.

And a fine nonsensical way to ramble on this was indeed. I'd be better employed reading about all the sights I had missed. But my guide-book was one of those infuriating French volumes with all its pages still uncut, save those on Nîmes and the first two on Lyons. And this seemed an excellent reason for leaving them like that. No sense in trying to be level-headed, anyway, sitting there, on a suitcase in a crowded corridor.

So I closed my eyes and tried not to think. And immediately I saw him again, running alongside the train. "Miss . . . My dear Miss . . . this business . . . it was you."

When the train steamed into the Châteaucreux Station of Saint Etienne, I leaned out to see if I could spot Françoise.

And there she was, fairly dancing up and down the platform looking for me. Behind her hurried Catherine in her best hat and coat, carrying a very smart yellow leather valise.

And Françoise fell on me and cried oh-la, if I hadn't been on that train she would have suffocated with emotion, for wasn't it marvellous, that American lady Van Winkle had been most business-like; she had absolutely hustled Catherine into promising to catch the six-twenty-six to Paris; she was sending a car to meet her at the other end if I pleased; she was booking a room for her in her own hotel for the night; and tomorrow morning they were going to discuss things; and for the love of heaven, hurry, hurry, the Paris express was in.

So we tore over to the waiting express, and Catherine climbed in.

"Second class, I'll have you observe," said Françoise. "No thirds on this high-class rapid."

Then Catherine, who so far had not been able to get a word in edgeways, leaned from the window, her dark eyes very troubled.

"Françoise," she said, "it's no use. I can't help worrying. It's all so sudden, so fantastic. If I do get this job . . ."

"Name of a pipe!" stormed Françoise. "I've told you! I've spent the whole day telling you. I'll be all right. Trust me to enjoy my little self in my own way. You just think of all those dollars you may be able to earn, all those places you'll be able to see. And listen, don't forget to send that telegram."

So she rattled on, not giving Catherine a chance, till the train moved off, and left us waving on the platform.

Then she turned to me. "Dor-o-tee," she said wearily, "I now understand a little how hard the good God must work to talk any of us into trying His bright Paradise."

And when I looked, I saw her eyes were full of tears, her face suddenly very drawn and tired.

"Come on," she said, and without another word we walked out of the station.

"Permit me, Miss Dor-o-tee," said a polite voice, and there was Monsieur Frécon waiting on the pavement, insisting on carrying my suitcase.

"I heard about this surprising letter from England," he began.

"I sent Catherine to borrow his valise," put in my forthright cousin. "It's a beauty, as you saw, and there's nothing like making a good impression."

"It belonged to my mother," said Monsieur Frécon. "She liked everything of the best."

Well, as Françoise said later, having borrowed his grand valise, we just had to invite him in to supper. He accepted immediately, and as we whipped up an omelette Françoise commented in great detail on everything Miss Clarkson had told us about Mrs. Luvisa Van Winkle.

Presently, however, Monsieur Frécon asked what I thought of Lyons, and I most truthfully said I had enjoyed my day there very much indeed. Whereupon they both snorted that I needn't talk to them about Lyons. Why, that fine city had the impudence to look down its clean nose on Saint Etienne! Liked to treat it as a dirty but useful sort of suburb! But Saint Etienne knew how to reply, they could tell me! Saint Etienne stood no highfalutin nonsense from Lyons. Suburb indeed!

And back we went to Mrs. Luvisa Van Winkle again; and other rich Americans and their ways.

Not one of us, of course, had ever been to America or set eyes on a rich American; but trifles like that do not put French people off a good conversation. After all, there is nothing quite so stimulating and delightful as laying the law down about something nobody knows anything about.

Then Françoise told us how at one time Catherine could never pass a travel agency without going in to collect a bundle of leaflets for the pure pleasure of reading about places she could never hope to see.

"I tell you," cried Françoise, "if she goes with this American lady, it will be a dream, a beautiful dream come true."

And I said, well, why not? Dreams did sometimes come true. The proof? There I was, sitting right there, with my family, in France.

At this, Françoise got up, went to the cupboard behind me, and brought out a bottle of some digestive liqueur that she had made herself.

"There!" she said, and handed us each a little glass. "I'd like the news about that, if you please. Just taste me that!"

So I tasted it, and said, well, if she insisted on the truth, it tasted to me precious like a powerful cough cure that I quite enjoyed when a child.

And Françoise shrieked, ah no, of all the base slanders from Perfidious Albion; and drink it up, would I, it was superb for the digestion. Everyone said so, and we all looked as if we needed it after the day's rush and excitement.

Monsieur Frécon, however, rose to his feet. And I can't explain it, but suddenly he wasn't a homely, diffident little man any longer. There was a strange, a most touching dignity about him.

"To all our dreams!" he said quietly, and raised his glass. "May they all come true!"

And we drank to this, and shook hands all round, very soberly, very solemnly.

Then Françoise, most abruptly I thought, practically

ordered poor Monsieur Frécon to go home. And he reluctantly found his hat and went, saying that he would look in tomorrow, if he might, to hear how Catherine had got on.

The next day was very different. The hours simply crawled by, all the longer because Françoise and I found it quite impossible to settle down to anything. We made the beds; we flicked a duster here and there; we waved a mop over the floors; we said the same things over and over again; and we drank endless cups of tea. I made it— Françoise still clung to her theory that tea improved if soaked first in a little cold water.

Towards six that evening when Françoise was declaring that we had better go out for a brisk canter or she'd start foaming at the mouth, there was a loud bang on the door. And there it was, the telegram we were so feverishly expecting.

"Meet midnight train. Catherine."

"Ah, no!" exploded Françoise. "This is about as soothing as a poultice on a wooden leg! We still know nothing! She doesn't say yes, she goes. She doesn't say no, she doesn't go. Put your fingers in your ears, Dor-o-tee. I am going to treat myself to a good loud scream!"

But at that moment Monsieur Frécon came in and insisted on taking us out and treating us to a meal instead, a very good meal, too, in a very pleasant restaurant.

Then we took a stroll down to the Place Marengo again and sat down outside a café to take our coffee.

But we were all strangely quiet that evening; even Françoise had nothing to say.

By and by the stars came out, and a warm breeze sprang up and danced in the great trees, and from the little bandstand came the strains of my favourite song, "Ma Normandie".

Françoise hummed it for a moment, then broke off. "They can say what they like," she said, as if clinching an argument, "but it's a good place, our dirty old Saint Etienne. People come here, tears streaming down their faces, swearing they won't stay a day longer once they've finished the accursed job that brought them here. And years later you meet them . . . still here . . . by choice."

"They become aware," said Monsieur Frécon, "that there's a heart beneath the grime. As one grows older, it is this that matters. What do you think, Miss Dor-o-tee?"

I nodded; but I thought that Mrs. Penny would have known how to sum up Saint Etienne—a place a body could feel at home in, that's what she would have said. But it was beyond me to translate the true essence of this into French. So I nodded again and left it at that.

Long before midnight, there we were, all three of us, buying platform tickets in the entrance hall of the station, which they call "la Salle des Pas Perdus"—the Room of the Lost Steps. And I reflected how exactly this pointed the difference between the British and the French. We patiently queue; they pace restlessly up and down.

Then up and down the platform we paced, till at long last, the train from Paris pulled in, and out stepped Catherine, very neat and composed, yellow valise in hand.

We rushed to greet her; Monsieur Frécon took charge of the suitcase; and Françoise cried, "We'll take a taxi.

Not every day one of us comes back from hobnobbing with rich Americans."

So Monsieur Frécon hailed a taxi, and off we drove, Catherine staving off all our torrent of questions with a firm "Wait! Do wait! I'll tell you everything when we get in."

And not a scrap of information did we get from her till we were home, sitting round the table, looking at her, waiting.

Then Catherine said, well, first of all, Mrs. Luvisa Van Winkle was charming, absolutely charming. A delightful person. About sixty-five, she would say, but one couldn't tell, she was so spruce and well turned-out and lively. And she definitely preferred a companion who could speak no English, as she adored talking French —amazing French it was, unbelievably American. And the wages she offered were unbelievably American, too. More than she and Françoise ever earned between them, even in a good month.

"But quick! In the name of heaven, quick!" implored Françoise. "Come to the point! Have you got the job? Did she engage you?"

"She wanted to," said Catherine. "But . . ."

"But what?" asked Françoise quietly.

"I said I must have a little time to think. I said I would send her a telegram tomorrow."

Françoise leaned across the table and took both her sister's hands.

"Listen, big silly one," she said, her voice very gentle and warm, "I know what is going on inside your head. You are saying to yourself that even if you send home most of those dollars, I am not the one to sit with my hands folded on my stomach, that I shall try to go on with the ribbons, that it takes two of us to set up the looms. And, above all, you are thinking that I shall be lonely, especially when our Dor-o-tee has to return to her school in England. And perhaps most of all you are remembering that you once promised Maman to be good to your fat little sister.

"Well, listen, I have something to tell you.

"I, too, have made a great decision. I am going to marry Benoit Frécon!"

We looked at her, stunned, speechless.

"Well," said Françoise sharply, "aren't you going to congratulate me instead of sitting there like so many mummies?"

"Oh, Françoise! Françoise!" choked Monsieur Frécon, and took her hand.

"You . . . you are going to marry him?" stuttered Catherine.

"Yes," said Françoise. "God knows he's asked me often enough. Haven't you, Benoit?"

"Oh yes," said Monsieur Frécon fervently. "Every Sunday for five years now, ever since my dear mother passed away; every Sunday as regular as clockwork. Except last Sunday when I really hadn't a chance. It has all been quite monotonous for poor Françoise. You may find it hard to believe, but for my size, I am really a most determined man."

That did it. We began to laugh. And to cry. Then we all kissed each other; and Françoise brought out another of her home-brewed bottles—this one tasted very like the strips of green angelica that Mrs. Penny used to put on our Christmas cake. And this gave me the oddest feeling. Then I knew what it was. Why, this was how I felt when I was a little girl, watching Mrs. Penny decorate our cake, helping her to put up the paper chains—festive but solemn, because something so lovely, so happy was in the air.

Then Françoise made some coffee and explained that she had always admired and *liked* Benoit, but just as another good cyclist, as one might say, not as a husband.

Until last Sunday. Then, when she saw him pedalling away behind our bus, grey with dust and devotion, why, boum went her heart, boum, BOUM!

"I shall never understand her!" cried the happy Benoit. "Never! The only time I do *not* propose to her, she accepts me!"

Yes, Catherine could go off with her American lady with a happy, carefree heart. Françoise and Benoit would get married very quietly and settle down in the roomy flat over his shop. When Catherine returned from her globe-trotting, there would be her room waiting for her. Then, if she liked, she could lend a hand in the shop. They might start one of these circulating libraries. Catherine was to keep her eyes open and notice what kind of books women liked reading.

As for the looms, well, Françoise and Benoit would sell them for what they could fetch. It would be a terrible wrench, of course; but it had to come sooner or later. No sense keeping them, filling up a whole room.

At this point in the joyous planning Benoit rose to his feet. "Now," he said, "I think we must say what we have in our hearts for Dor-o-tee here. But for her, all this—this happiness, this good fortune, might never have come to us."

They crowded about me, saying the kindest things, telling me over and over again that I would always be welcome, always, always!

And I tried to laugh, and said I shuddered to think how different my holiday would have been if I had been sensible enough to stop and see Paris before I took the train to Nîmes. I might never have set eyes on those obliging Scarlet Wolves—or on them!

"There's a moral to this, of course," said Françoise. "Always miss your train when you feel so inclined!"

We drank merrily to this; then Françoise clapped Benoit's hat on his head, briskly kissed him good night, and sent him off home, half-tipsy with happiness and home-brewed digestives.

And we went off to bed. But not to sleep.

Catherine, it seemed, lay awake telling herself it was true. All this was true. Yes, everything was true. Above all, Mrs. Van Winkle was true.

Françoise regretted to confess that she lay awake and gave but a passing tender thought to her Benoit; and then saw clear, and twice as horrid as by day, the pictures, photographs and certificates hanging all over the walls of Benoit's flat, all under glass and with gilt frames six inches thick and deep, so help her—his mother liking everything of the best, confound her.

And she plotted shattering but credible accidents, not only to these, but to all the massive china ornaments as well, giving herself three years to make a clean sweep of the lot, beginning with the framed Certificate of Primary Studies awarded to Benoit at the age of eleven years two months, and ending with a last triumphant catastrophe whilst dusting "Diana the Huntress and her Dogs" in pea-green marble that filled all the mantelpiece of the sitting-room.

And she would fling open the shutters of that dark tomb of a sitting-room and let in the dear light of day, and never mind fading the curtains, cushions and carpet.

Yes, back would go those heavy curtains, and she would whip off the bleak holland covers on the velvet chairs and sofa; she would sit firmly on those fat smug cushions; walk boldly on that prim carpet. Ah no! She was not going to be intimidated, bossed about, by a lot of furniture.

All this she would do, but with such gentle and consummate cunning that her Benoit would have no glimmering of her Three Year Plan of Destruction—only an increasing awareness that this was truly home, their own dear home.

And I lay awake despising myself for the grey, miserable fears that nagged away at the back of my mind and refused to be silenced. I thought of the future, *my* future. I would have to go home soon. I had got through a good three-quarters of my money—I had, of course, insisted on paying my share of the housekeeping. Then there was my fare back to consider, not to mention the couple of days I wanted to spend in Nîmes.

I told myself that I was a nasty ungrateful woman, lying there, grizzling. I'd had the most wonderful holiday.

Found my family. Made some wonderful friends. What more did I want?

And I fiercely shook up my pillow and ordered myself to count my blessings.

But I thought instead of my cousins and Benoit, and my heart grew warm again. They deserved all the happiness in the world, all three of them, bless them. And I began to make feverish calculations, trying to work out whether I should buy them presents now, or whether I had better wait till I was safely home, with a month's salary in my pocket.

Then when I did doze off, I dreamed I was stretching out both hands to a kind and most comforting fire; and that Miss Clarkson was there, too, of all people, her pale-blue eyes very chilly as she said, "You *do* realise, don't you, that this isn't your fire? Not yours, you must realise, not yours!"

"I know! I know!" I cried, and woke up.

And, to my dismay, my face was wet and cold with tears. Worse still, I couldn't find my handkerchief; and I didn't want to switch on the light in case I woke up my sleeping cousins.

15

We Rush Ourselves Off Our Feet

We were all up bright and early the next morning, and the moment we had swallowed our coffee we pushed back the cups and composed a polite telegram to Mrs. Van Winkle:

"Happy to accept post. Please inform date departure Paris. Respectful sentiments. Lombard."

Mrs. Van Winkle, it seemed, had been more than vague about dates. She had waved her jewelled and beautifully manicured hands and said she guessed she was now about to do just everything in Paris, from a look at that heavenly Mona Lisa in the Louvre to a meal in that cute old chestnut tree. And when Catherine asked which cute old tree, Mrs. Van Winkle said, why, the one in that place called Robinson where Mimi of the opera disported herself—when her tiny hands weren't too frozen, of course.

Oh yes, a very energetic and amusing traveller, Mrs. Van Winkle, and, judging from the list of Parisian sights she intended to "do", Catherine calculated it would be all of three weeks before they set off for Italy.

"And I'll need every minute," she declared. "Every single minute. When I think of all I have to do . . .!"

"Right!" said Françoise. "Start thinking right away. And while you're at it, we'll go and send that telegram and bring back something quick and easy for lunch!"

So we packed the dishes in the sink, and Françoise and I set off with the telegram and a string bag, whilst Catherine sat down with paper and pencil to compile a list of all the things she would want to pack.

We were just washing up after the quick, easy meal, and briskly arguing out the programme for the afternoon's shopping, when back came a telegram from Mrs. Van Winkle:

"Delighted. Expect you Friday. Leaving for Italy Saturday evening. Sending car meet train as before. Will fix passport here. Looking forward many happy days together. Van Winkle."

"Friday!" shrieked Catherine, and collapsed into a chair. "But that's the day after tomorrow! I can't do it! I simply CANNOT do it. Not if I light candles to all the saints in heaven, I can't! Everything to wash. My 'sweeter' to finish. And I wanted to look round for a grey 'trotter' like that one of Dor-o-tee's. I'll never be ready in time, never! I can't go half round the world as I am."

"Ah no!" said Françoise, very pale and shaken, too. "The woman must be doing Paris in one of those jets!" And she sat down, quite overcome, too.

Now people may scoff, but a seasoned schoolmistress can come in very handy at times. And this definitely was one of those times. So I promptly took charge. I looked at my two shattered cousins and said in the steely voice that had galvanised more than one Form 1C, that we had two whole days before us, that there were three of us, so this worked out to six whole days between us, and if an American woman of sixty-five could hustle with such purpose and speed, so, I assumed, could we. So what about cutting short the anguished despair, and bringing out the washing instead.

It worked. In less than ten minutes Catherine was feverishly knitting away, finishing off the neck of her new "sweater"—which my cousins always insisted was elegant English for a knitted sweater—a jumper to me. And Françoise and I tore into the washing, and pegged it all up in the little courtyard at the back of the house. It was a warm sunny day, so everything dried in record time. We then borrowed another flat-iron from a sympathetic neighbour; and the two of us tackled the ironing. And they both laughed their heads off when I insisted on hanging all the freshly ironed clothes on the backs of chairs to air off in the warm sun streaming through the open windows. They had never heard of this British ritual; and Catherine, casting off the "sweater", asked, "Tell me, Dor-o-tee, this airing, is it good for me, or my petticoats?"

"Both," I said, and brought out the "trotter"—my grey tweed costume. "Come on," I ordered. "Try this on."

As I thought, it fitted her beautifully, just needed the hem letting down. "The woman's such a giraffe," said Françoise and beat a hasty retreat as Catherine and I then began a first-class French set-to.

No, no, one thousand times no, Catherine was not going to take my grey trotter. She would not dream of such a thing. Certainly not. No, no, and NO.

And when she paused for breath, I acidly requested her to stop holding up things and get out of that skirt. Then in came Benoit, and was warmly greeted by Françoise. "Ah no! Clear out, will you? We can't do with a man about the place. Oh, but wait a minute. Just fly out and get us a loaf, there's a dear kind angel!"

Out flew Benoit and came back with a long loaf under one arm, and, being a French angel, a couple of bottles under the other. And Françoise set plates and glasses on the table and I cut us all some real English sandwiches, and not, as I took pains to point out, hunks of bread hacked off at the double with something slapped between them which they had the French nerve to call a "sondeveech".

"Quite good," said Benoit, taking his fourth. "But simply no exercise for the teeth and jaws."

Then Catherine suddenly pushed back her plate, reached for her list, and crossed out another item.

"The evening dress," she said mournfully. "There simply isn't the time to make one; and they cost the earth ready-made."

It seemed that Mrs. Van Winkle had told her that American women adored wearing long evening gowns, that they positively jumped at every chance to wear them. "And quite right, too," Mrs. Van Winkle had said. "There's nothing half so becoming to any woman, no matter what age. So do bring one, my dear."

Yes, do bring one, just like that, as if Catherine only

had to select one from the half-dozen or so that were surely hanging up in her wardrobe.

"I had thought of blue velvet," mourned Catherine. "I have always fancied myself in a long gown of velvet. Deep-blue velvet. So distinguished, but so wearable."

"Velvet!" exclaimed Benoit. "Deep-blue velvet!" He pushed back his chair, reached for his hat, mumbled something about back in a few minutes, and bolted.

"Ah no! We only need this!" cried Françoise. "We only need him to feel sick now!"

But in less than a quarter of an hour Benoit was back, and this time he was carrying a bulky untidy parcel, hastily wrapped in a white tablecloth.

"From the sitting-room windows," he panted. "They're as good as new, and lined, so I don't think they're faded. Besides, we have always kept the shutters closed."

He unrolled the sheet; and there inside was a pair of long curtains, velvet curtains, of a deep rich blue.

"No, no," said Benoit, shaking them out and examining them. "No, they haven't faded anywhere. They would make quite a nice dress, don't you think?"

And there he stood, holding out the curtains, looking at us, so anxious, so eager, that Françoise flung both arms about him.

"Oh, Benoit!" she choked. "Dear old Benoit!"

"But, Benoit . . ." said Catherine, very moved, too. "But, Benoit . . ."

"They're lovely, lovely!" rushed in Françoise, stroking them tenderly. "Such beautiful velvet! Fit for a queen!"

"Yes," said Benoit happily. "That is what my poor

Maman always said. She always liked everything of the best."

"Bless her!" said Françoise, her eyes very bright and warm. "Oh, bless her!"

"But, Benoit," said Catherine again, "it's so good of you, so very good, but . . ."

"Of course there will be time," cried Françoise. "We'll just make the time. We will unpick them tonight, and tomorrow morning at crack of dawn, at nine o'clock sharp, the moment her shop opens, we'll be waiting on the doorstep to talk to Madame Faure. Now look, do look!"

She draped the curtains over Catherine's shoulders, tied them in at the waist with Benoit's tie, and we all stood back and agreed that she was going to look wonderful, absolutely Rue de la Paix, worth a thousand dollars, in fact. Whereupon Benoit uncorked his second bottle and we all drank to yet another family victory.

Then the discussion broke out again and raged merrily on and on. Tomorrow morning we would buy a wonderful paper pattern from this Madame Faure who ran an Institute of Cut, and who had both "chic" and a sympathetic heart. Every stitch, of course, was going to be done by hand. One didn't crush such celestial velvet in a mundane sewing-machine. There was a stall down on the Place des Ursules where one could buy evening slippers of every size and colour. Françoise would go there and bargain for a pair. And now, Benoit was please to go home, and not show his dear kind nose inside the door till half-past eight tomorrow evening, when he would see—what he would see.

With this, we all three embraced our Benoit, wished him good night, and packed him off home.

And we spread an old sheet on the table and sat down to the curtains.

At a quarter to nine next morning there we were, waiting with the curtains, on the doorstep of the Institute of Cut, gazing at three wax ladies with tousled hair, clad in smart pink paper costumes, smiling coyly in the window.

A large notice glued on the door said that for five hundred francs Madame Faure would cut out a paper pattern of any known garment, guaranteed to fit the most difficult figure like a glove.

For a further two hundred francs Madame Faure would tack together this pattern and the client could try it on and see the effect for herself before leaving the shop.

For a net outlay of one thousand five hundred francs Madame Faure would cut out, tack together, and carefully fit a strong canvas pattern of any garment, which, if more expensive, was absolutely fool-proof and therefore most warmly recommended to all amateur dressmakers.

A polite note in red ink at the foot of this notice said that the Institute of Cut regretted to inform clients that to all the prices quoted above they must now add fifty per cent increase due to rising costs which Madame Faure wished to make clear were entirely beyond her control.

At nine sharp the door of the Institute of Cut opened, and a startled lady, still in her dressing-gown, threw up both hands as we charged in, unpacking the curtains and explaining as we went. Quickly grasping the urgency of our case, however, she listened with sympathetic interest. Then she examined the curtains, exclaimed at their quality and rich colour, and asked us to sit down for a moment whilst she got into her dress.

So we sat down, and almost immediately back came Madame buttoning up her smart black frock, whipped out a tape-measure, and took a long, long look at Catherine.

At half-past nine, Catherine, clad from head to foot in pink tissue paper, stood tense and motionless, as Madame, her mouth full of pins, danced round her, making deft amendments to neck, waist and sleeves.

At a quarter-past ten, Madame, now absolutely one of the family, knowing all about me and Miss Clarkson and Mrs. Van Winkle, was offering to cut out the velvet, crying that it would be a black crime if this so-lovely pile did not ripple deep and true from Mademoiselle's neck to her toes.

At eleven o'clock we were counting out the paper notes to pay Madame, and thanking her most warmly, as she packed up our parcel with many last-minute instructions for completing her masterpiece.

Then Catherine and I bore it home whilst Françoise raced off to the Place des Ursules, a cutting of the velvet in her hand, to bargain for the pair of evening shoes.

We were just laying the table for a quick snack when she returned—triumphant. "Good old Place des Ursules!" she cried. "I've found them! Look, the very colour! A lovely match! Now come on, let's swallow a mouthful and get on with it!"

So we bolted our salad and chips and whisked the

dishes, unwashed into the sink; Catherine got into her dressing-gown so as not to waste time dressing and undressing every time we fitted her; and we spread the old sheet on the table again, pulled up our chairs, threaded our needles and prepared to sew for our lives.

"I've thought it all out," said Françoise. "Mass-production methods, of course, as in America. I'll tackle the front. Dor-o-tee, you make the sleeves; and Catherine, you start on the back."

At five o'clock, my sleeves finished, I made some tea. I felt we all needed it. Even Catherine, who detested tea, drank a second cup with grim determination, saying she only hoped it would perform all that was claimed on the label, and truly revive the drooping.

At eight o'clock the gown was finished, and we reverently carried it, swathed in the sheet, into my bedroom and hung it on the door. Then Catherine retired to the dark cupboard to perform "la grande toilette"—a good wash all over in a very small bath with a generous dash of eau-de-Cologne. Presently out she came, as glowing and fresh as if she'd stepped from a gleaming bathroom all marble and chrome, and shot into my bedroom just as Benoit came walking in.

"Wait there!" she cried. "Just wait there, all three of you! I won't be long."

So Benoit, Françoise and I sat and waited till the door flew open again.

And there stood my cousin Catherine—transformed.

"Why, Catherine!" whispered Françoise. "My little Catherine!"

"Beautiful!" cried Benoit. "Beautiful!"

"Yes," said Catherine quietly. "The most beautiful frock I shall ever have."

She turned slowly round so that we might admire the side view and the back.

In the darkening room she seemed to glow from her shining dark hair to the satin slippers on her feet. And we watched her—silent, amazed, and very moved at her new assurance, her dignity, her quiet elegance in that softly flowing velvet gown.

The sound of voices coming up the stairs shattered the spell.

"Mon Dieu!" gasped Benoit and clasped his head. "The Friends of the Pedal! They're all calling in to see you! I completely forgot to tell you!"

"What!" shrieked Françoise. "Oh, you triple lunatic! Take off that dress, Catherine. Dor-o-tee, for the love of heaven, help me clear up this room. Benoit, don't stand there gaping like a fish, get out the glasses, bring in the chairs. Hurry, all of you, hurry, hurry!"

So we flew round tidying up the room; and the Friends of the Pedal came pouring in; and everybody shook hands with everybody else, and found a seat somewhere, most of us two to a chair. Then Monsieur Martin, the President, called for silence and made a most graceful little speech. He said he knew he spoke for all the Friends of the Pedal when he said that on hearing the wonderful and surprising news that Catherine was about to travel far across the globe they were all torn between two conflicting emotions: sorrow at losing so loyal and charming a cycling-comrade, and joy to think that she was going to speed along far-distant roads, with no hard pedalling either, but most luxuriously free-wheel all the way as one might say.

Then he begged Catherine to accept a gift from them all. It was not very large, but it was bursting with all their warmest good wishes. And he held out a handbag, a handsome brown hide one with a businesslike shoulder strap. As Madame Martin pointed out, any amount could be stowed away inside, and yet Catherine would have both hands free to wave the passports and tip those brigands of porters.

Catherine was far too moved to do more than stutter, "Oh, thank you, thank you!"

But Françoise promptly ordered half a dozen of us to move our chairs for a moment whilst she unlocked the bottom cupboard of the dresser and got out a couple of very special bottles that their mother had hidden away for just such happy occasions.

Then Françoise gave Benoit a meaning nudge, and he got up and cleared his throat and announced that he, too, had a piece of happy news to tell them—he and Françoise had decided to ride together through the rest of their lives on a bicycle built for two. Yes, from now on, it was a tandem for Françoise and him. When the cheering died down, Monsieur Martin made another little speech, and Benoit replied. Then somebody else proposed a toast; and soon speech followed speech as we all warmed to our own eloquence and my Aunt Mariette-Louise's red-letter bottles. In fact it was all of twelve o'clock before the Friends of the Pedal shook hands for the last time and went off home, still calling good wishes as they went down the street.

Then Françoise and I made Catherine go straight off
to bed, and we set to and washed up the glasses. Suddenly
Françoise sat down; and I wasn't at all sure whether she
was laughing or crying.

"Dor-o-tee," she said, "I've just remembered something. I must tell you."

"Do," I said, and sat down, too.

Françoise wiped her eyes on the tea-towel and said,
well, when they were little girls, a big girl called
Germaine in the flat upstairs managed to scrape through
the examination for the Certificate of Proficiency of the
Practical School of Commerce and Industry. And her
proud Papa and Maman, as a reward, presented her with
a bicycle. Oh, not a new one, of course. Indeed the
handle-bar was so lofty that she just had to sit bolt up-
right or it would have dislocated her neck. But it *was* a
bicycle. And Catherine used to stand and gaze at it, lost
in longing.

But Catherine, of course, was expected to wait for her
bicycle till she reached the same ripe age and advanced
level of scholarship. In those days, one did not present
bicycles to mere nine-year-olds in the second class of
their primary school. No, indeed!

But young Catherine decided not to wait. Already the
lure of distant roads, the love of travel were stirring in
her breast. But she knew, however, that it is often a
waste of a child's breath and time to wait on parents. So
she took her case to the very highest court. She went
straight to the saints of Paradise!

Yes, night after night, Catherine lay in bed and offered
up fervent petition to all the saints, particularly the more

travelled among them, imploring them, badgering them to join their celestial voices with hers as she prayed, "Please, I want a bicycle. I do so want a bicycle. It needn't be a new one. A secondhand one will do, but not so tall as Germaine's, because I'm only nine. Please, please, a bicycle, a bicycle just my size. Saint Paul, pray for my bicycle. Saint Antoine pray for me. Pray for my bicycle. Amen. Amen."

Of course Papa and Maman let her pray. One does not discourage the devotions and faith of a pious little nine-year-old, even if she does pray aloud and her bedroom is next door to the living-room. One hesitates to suggest that silent prayer is perhaps as efficacious, not to a nine-year-old who does not realise that walls are so thin.

So night after night Catherine loudly prayed herself to sleep. "Please, please a bicycle! Saint Paul, pray for my bicycle. Saint Christopher, pray for my bicycle. Saint Paul, pray for my bicycle."

And one evening, Papa, yearning once again to read his paper in slippered quiet, suddenly turned to Maman and hissed, "Mariette-Louise, for the love of heaven, let us buy that child her damn bicycle before I lose my reason —and smother her in her pillows!"

So Catherine got her bicycle; and, as Papa ruefully pointed out to Maman, they received the very briefest of thanks as she rushed straight out to buy tall candles for all those obliging saints of hers, and returned with practically every girl in the second class who stood two deep on the pavement to watch her mount her bicycle and wobble off down the street, bound at last for the alluring, beautiful roads that stretched out and beyond the Quarter of the Ribbon-makers.

"And now," said Françoise, blowing her nose, "she goes to Italy, Egypt, Australia and New York. Say what you like, Dor-o-tee, life can be very strange—and beautiful."

I agreed, and we got up, finished off the glasses, kissed each other, and staggered, at last, to bed.

The next day, Friday, tore by at the most amazing speed. Every soul my cousins knew, and they knew a great many, called in to wish Catherine "Bon voyage". And, of course, we had to offer them a little refreshment; and no sooner had we washed up after one batch of visitors, than in would walk another lot. We packed Catherine's cases as best we could; and before we knew it, there was Benoit waiting at the door with a taxi. In we got, very touched to see all the neighbours standing in their doorways or hanging from their windows, waving and calling, "Bon voyage! Good luck!" And off we drove, waving back, as Françoise said, for all the world like British royalty.

And at six-thirty precisely that Friday evening, Benoit, Françoise and I stood on the platform of the Châteaucreux Station of Saint Etienne and waved my cousin Catherine off to Paris and her new life. And she leaned from the window, very smart in the grey "trotter", the handsome handbag slung on one shoulder, her eyes shining like stars, as she called "Thank you, my dears! Thank you! Oh, thank you!"

Then we walked home, quiet, subdued, and suddenly dog-tired. But scarcely had we shut the door behind us, than there was another loud, urgent bang.

"Ah, no!" groaned Françoise. "Not another visitor!"

It wasn't. It was another telegram—for me this time. I tore it open, and burst out laughing.

My telegram ran:

"Julius Caesar in Nîmes tomorrow, Saturday. You must not miss him. Letter in post to explain all. Cordial handshakes. Durand. Nîmes."

16

Julius Caesar in Nîmes

The letter to explain all turned up by the first post next morning with "Express! Urgent: Deliver at once!" stamped all over it. And it did everything except explain.

Monsieur Durand said he regretted infinitely giving me so short notice, but to tell the truth, although he had a big poster in the window, he had thought that everything was starting in a fortnight's time. But it wasn't. It was starting right away. And it would be so particularly interesting for me on Saturday—which, of course, was that very day—that he had taken the liberty to get me a seat, a very good one, where I could see everything. So he did hope I would be able to come. Indeed he and the regulars were all counting on seeing me there in time for dinner that night, as they had worked out that my best trains, indeed my only trains were the twelve past ten to Lyons, from there the twelve-twenty in the direction of Marseilles, from which I was to alight with all speed at Avignon so as to catch the sixteen-hours-twenty-five in the direction of Perpignan which stopped at Nîmes at seventeen-fifteen.

And, till tonight then, with friendliest greetings from them all, he was mine sincerely, Marius Durand.

Then came a P.S.

"I enclose a leaflet."

Well, as I said to Françoise, it was just as well he did, for the leaflet certainly did explain all—and with the utmost dignity, too.

Below a very fine picture of the Arena it announced that the Roman City of Nîmes, the City of Classical Art, the Centre of the Vineyards of Provence, was to celebrate the Coming of Summer with a Grand Festival of Music, Dance, and Drama.

And that very night, in that unique setting, the Arena —bequeathed to them by Antiquity, the ancient glory of Nîmes was to shine again in a grand performance of *Julius Caesar* by William Shakespeare so justly known to his compatriots as "the great Will"; caste of one hundred and eighty, two hundred costumes; seats—one hundred francs to four hundred francs.

"You'll go, of course," decided Françoise.

"Well, I suppose I'd better," I said, "as he's bought that seat. But really, the way you French rush people off their feet . . .!"

"Dor-o-tee," said Françoise, "something tells me here, in my French heart, that we shall be very happy one day we rushed ourselves off our feet."

And I said something told me here in my British common sense that I had better take my small suitcase, as it certainly looked as if I'd have to spend the night in Nîmes. According to the leaflet, the play was not due to start until twenty-one hours, and that meant nine p.m to me.

At twelve past ten, then, there I was with my small

suitcase in the train heading for Lyons. Françoise, trusting nobody when it came to time-tables, had checked up on the regulars and had said, yes, they were right, it *was* one of these comic cross-country journeys. Mrs. Van Winkle herself could not do it under seven hours three minutes even if every train shot in dead on time, which was most unlikely.

It was a long and most miserable journey. Not that I minded the jumping in and out of trains. I almost welcomed that. It made a break. But there was no break in the grey monotonous circle of my thoughts.

One side of me, far too bright, far too earnest, harped on and on, "Now this is going to be something right out of the ordinary, something to talk about when you go back to teaching. Think of it! *Julius Caesar*, acted in French, in an arena built by the Romans themselves!"

But the other side of me savagely refused to be bright, refused to be earnest, refused to cheer up and think joyfully of going back, taking up my old life once more.

It wasn't that I hated the thought of teaching again. I wasn't an unsuccessful teacher in my own little way. I hadn't been brought up in Aunt Kate's school for nothing. I got on with the children all right.

It was the thought of going home after a day's work, opening the door, and finding no one—no one of my own.

Especially now. Oh, especially now!

"You're a fine one!" I sharply told myself. "You've done everything you ever dreamed of doing. What more do you want?"

And I tried to think sensibly of going back, to tell myself

how fortunate I was to have such a safe job, with long holidays, and a pension at the end of it, too.

But it was no use. Round and round ground my thoughts in the same arid circle for seven grey hours and thirty minutes—the train was late, of course.

But when I arrived at last at the Café-Restaurant des Monuments the whole world seemed to grow kind and warm again. Little Pierre waiting in the doorway spotted me as I turned the corner, and came flying to meet me, and hugged and hugged me. Monsieur Durand came hurrying out to shake hands with me; and Angélique tore down the stairs and insisted on carrying my small suitcase up to my room—room seven again, I was delighted to see.

And on the way up, she told me how that young man of hers, Placide from Marseilles, had turned out a proper camel if ever there was one. He'd disappeared completely now, with the seven thousand francs she'd given him towards their happy home, not to mention the two blankets—all wool—she'd been fool enough to lend him last winter. But that was life, that was, said Angélique, and a girl sometimes had to learn the hard way. So no more passionate good-lookers for Angélique. Ah no!

And strictly between ourselves, she now had her eye on a little barber; nothing sensational about him, exasperatingly cool and collected, in fact. And a good thing, too. An up-and-coming barber with a small business of his own could not afford to raise Cain every time he had a row with his girl, or he might well find himself one day slitting his best customer's throat. And that, said Angélique, would hardly be good for business.

I said, no indeed; nor for the best customer either.

And with that, Angélique went down to lend a hand with the dinner.

When I went down, there were all the regulars—Madame Muraton, Monsieur Labise, Monsieur Espérandier, Monsieur Olivon, and Monsieur Pinatel—all waiting to shake hands with me, all warmly delighted to see me again. And the little tables were already pushed together and laid ready for dinner; and there in the centre stood a jug stuffed tight with carnations—I had once said how I loved carnations. And Pierre was allowed to sit up and have dinner with us, and Monsieur Tallon, the photographer, and his wife had also been invited. And they told me that their grandmama had instructed their Aunt Pélagie to write and say that she was glad to hear the granddaughter of Marius Durand had had the sense to seek out her family in France. And this, of course, had given Aunt Pélagie a wonderful opening for three whole pages beginning, "Alas!", and giving her opinions on family-life today; all of which they just had to read because she had a way of slipping in real items of news between the wedges of sermon.

The dinner, too, was very special, though I can't for the life of me recall what we had; and when the coffee came in, I looked up at the clock and exclaimed that I'd better get my coat on—*Julius Caesar* was due to start in a quarter of an hour. The regulars said, nonsense, he wouldn't be all that punctual; there was plenty of time to drink my coffee.

But Monsieur Durand, however, muttered something and charged upstairs; and Monsieur Pinatel turned to me and said, "Well, Miss, we hope you admired it?"

"Admired what?" I asked.

"Why, the new costume-sport I made for Marius, of course! He got me to make it specially for that trip of his up to Lyons. And I've never known him so fussy. Wanted it to fit this time if you please! Said he wanted to look West End! By heaven, here he comes in it! Now, where's he off to?"

Down the stairs came Monsieur Durand, still in his slippers, but wearing the new brown tweed suit he had worn that day in Lyons. In one hand he carried his new biscuit-coloured hat, in the other his new yellow shoes.

The regulars gaped, then set up a cheer, inquiring if he was off to try his luck with Mademoiselle Shéhérazade of the Palace of a Thousand Varieties—a very well-known young lady, I gathered, who liked her gentlemen friends dressy as well as generous.

Monsieur Durand, putting on his new shoes with the help of a tablespoon, said haughtily that he did not expect them to believe it, of course—being such a deplorably uncultivated lot—but *he* was interested in William Shakespeare, and, if they must know, he was off to see this Julius Caesar, too.

And he turned to me and said, "So we'll go together, eh, Miss?"

"With pleasure," I said, and ran up to get my coat. And we set off, leaving the regulars playing cards and furiously arguing whether Shakespeare wrote plays, or operas with music, or both.

Monsieur Durand had taken two seats on the ground

floor of the Arena, the great oval floor on which the
gladiators once fought. No stage had been set up, but a
whole quarter of the Arena had been roped off, and there,
facing us, towered a statue of Pompey, at least sixty feet
high, I should say. Wide gangways between the blocks
of seats led to this vast space; and that was all. No scenery,
no trappings of any kind. The stone seats rising tier on
tier, the great oval archways, the breathtaking sweep of
massive wall lay before us, uncluttered, waiting.

The rest of the Arena, however, was filling up fast.
Crowds were pouring into the stone seats, and the
clamour of voices grew and grew. But at nine o'clock a
sudden silence fell as the loudspeakers gave a polite,
apologetic cough and announced, "Ladies and gentlemen, there will be a little delay. We must wait till it is
quite dark."

The citizens of Nîmes, being true Provençals, were not
prepared to let that pass without a few hearty groans. But
we settled down amiably enough. After all, one can
always talk. And the summer sky darkened and a star or
two came out; and voices began to call, "Well, how much
darker do you want it?"

So the loudspeakers apologised again, saying there had
been a regrettable technical hitch. . . .

But we drowned the rest in our massed opinion of all
technical hitches.

It was all of ten o'clock, and very dark, when there was
a great burst of music. And we caught our breath as
down the gangways raced six magnificent negroes carrying
flaming torches, and set them about Pompey's statue.
And in their strange, portentous blaze, the play began.

We did not watch it. We did far more than that. We joined in. We *lived* that great tragedy. At times we even rose to take charge. As on that storm-rent night when the conspirators decide to murder Caesar and have done with it; and we sat there, shaken to the soul, the thunder muttering and crashing about us, the lightning streaking overhead, lighting up the whole Arena.

But when the thunder began to drown the voices of Casca and Cicero, a voice high in the stone seats spoke up for us all. "Go easy with that thunder!" it yelled. And we all took up the cry, "Assez! Assez!" till the gentlemen enjoying themselves rolling out the thunderbolts heard us at last, and to a very subdued rumbling we settled down again to hear what Casca thought of the night.

Now I would hate to give the impression that it was all rather funny. It wasn't. Far from it. The play was magnificently acted. At moments it was unbearably moving: the soothsayer coming down the gangway between us, his hand on the shoulder of a little lad, sightless eyes turned to the dark sky, crying "César! César!", Portia pleading with Brutus, begging to know what was in his tortured heart.

And when Caesar, mortally wounded, stood at bay, his back to Pompey's statue, the conspirators closing in on him, it was we who cried "A-ah!" And Caesar, hearing *us*, looked up; and saw Brutus on the steps above him, dagger raised high. And crying "Et toi, Brutus!" great Caesar died—so magnificently that we all rose to our feet and clapped and clapped. Here, by heaven, was a man who knew how to die!

Then when Mark Antony gave his funeral oration, it

was to us he spoke, to us, sitting there, row upon row, in the darkness. It was to us he showed Caesar's mantle, the cruel gashes, the great stains of blood.

It was to us he cried, "Kind souls, what, weep you when you but behold our Caesar's vesture wounded? Look you here, here is himself, marr'd as you see, by traitors!"

Oh, we were with them, those citizens of Rome, as they went tearing over the stone seats, shouting mutiny and revenge.

Then came the night before the Battle of Philippi when Brutus, tormented by doubt, desperately unhappy, takes up his book and tries to read. "Let me see, let me see. Is not the page turned down where I left reading?"

But we gasped "Ah!", for we had seen it, high against the topmost wall; and Brutus, hearing us, looked up; and saw it, too, blazing there against the dark sky—Caesar's ghost, cold and menacing.

Then, of course, with a whole quarter of the Arena to move about in, and any number of soldiers on either side, the battle scenes were terrific.

"They know how to fight, eh?" said Monsieur Durand. "You know who they are, of course? Our local air-force boys."

Well, they might have been air-force boys every other night of the week, but that night they were Romans, sword in hand, fighting mad, tearing over the tiers of stone seats, flying for their lives down every gangway.

I turned to say that I had never realised Shakespeare could be so exciting, when Monsieur Durand took my hand. Even in the darkness, I could see his face was very pale.

"Miss," he said, "I must apologise to your Shakespeare,

but I cannot support him another moment. I must say what I have in my heart.

"Please . . . please tell me . . . do you like me?"

"Yes," I said. "Yes. Of course I do."

"Enough . . . enough to marry me?"

"Yes," I said. "Oh yes!"

And there we sat, hand in hand; and the Battle of Philippi raged all about and we did not hear a thing—only the singing in our hearts.

And suddenly, why, there was Mark Antony standing over the body of poor Brutus—and I had not even seen him die. And he was crying, "This was a man!"

That brought us to our feet, and we clapped and cheered; and the lights went up, and we poured out into the quiet streets.

Most of us made for the nearest café calling for something to calm our emotions—we had a job to find a table. And as we sat down, I looked at my watch, and was staggered to see it was one o'clock. But nobody seemed to care about that. All around me I could hear them: "Formidable, eh, ce Shaks-peer! Et Jules César donc! Et Cassius, quel type! Ah non, superbe, superbe!"

Yes, "the great Will" had certainly made another hit; chained another victory to his car. It was reported next day that fifteen thousand of us had packed the great Arena that night.

Then we walked slowly home; and as we went, Marius spoke of his wife, how kind she was; how she had always said, "If anything ever happens to me, you must marry again. I don't want you to live alone. Promise me you will marry again—such a compliment to me."

But he had thought there could never be another woman; yet, there I was walking by his side.

And I longed to say how deeply I cared, but all I could say was, "My dear! My dear!"

Then I said, well, weren't we a pair, both of us getting on for fifty, and strolling along as if we were sweet and twenty.

And he stopped. And put both hands on my shoulders.

"Dor-o-tee," he said, "why must you women always think that love is only for the young? When I was in my beautiful twenties, I was always falling in love; in-out, in-out, enough to make the head spin. Always mad with being so happy; or mad with being so unhappy. But now, I don't want to feel mad any more. I want someone who will hear me shout too much, talk too much, and love me just the same . . . even if I am a little fat and not at all beautiful."

I said I liked him just as he was, and that I wasn't exactly an oil-painting myself.

But he had never heard of this expression, for he said quite seriously, no, but perhaps I had a good photograph I could give him. And I didn't bother to explain, but took his arm instead; and we walked on, and overhead the kind stars danced . . . thousands of them.

When we got in, Marius sank down on the nearest chair and pulled off his yellow shoes. "Oof!" he said. "Now my poor feet can be 'appy, too. Dor-o-tee, did you see what I did with my slippers?"

17

The Family Album Takes Up the Story

Last night I lay awake wondering how best to tell the rest of my story; and for some strange unaccountable reason found myself thinking instead of winter evenings in days gone by, the long winter evenings by the fire when I was a child, listening to Mrs. Penny's tales of Sam Small, the pedlar.

And I remembered how I would insist on hearing again and again the entrancing details of Sam's wares, the homely familiar ones and the bright new novelties, before I allowed Mrs. Penny to go on and tell how they would examine them all, taking their time, till presently Sam sat down to a handsome dish of bacon and eggs and a quart pot of strong tea; and they all settled down round him to catch up with the news. For Sam was a powerful talker, better than any newspaper, and with a rare memory, so that it was a fair treat, a proper education, just to sit there and hear him tell of the old happenings that always lay deep at the root of the new.

Then suddenly I saw quite clearly that there was no need for me to fuss and fret for words to unpack my heart, no need to wonder how I would find the words to tell so little more and yet say so much.

There, in the pages of my Family Album, was all my

story—the old happenings and the shining happy new. I had only to open it, and there they all were. I could leave everything to them. They would speak for themselves.

So today, as I write, it lies on the table before me—my Family Album.

And as I look at it, so battered now and so beloved, I remember again the night Aunt Kate gave it to me, very new and bright, touchingly new and bright—and half empty.

And I remember how I secretly vowed that I would go on with it, yes, I would fill all those glossy pages, those empty waiting spaces, just as *they* would have done— my father and mother—if only they'd had the chance, the time.

Then as the years went by, if ever I remembered this solemn youthful vow, I would look at it, still half empty, its bright covers slowly fading, and tell myself bitterly that even the most devoted school-teacher draws the line at filling a Family Album with portraits of Heads, Staff, and a rotation of Form 1C.

Yet here, on the very first of those empty pages, I have the photograph presented to me by my last Form 1C.

"Please, Miss Durand, to remind you of us. And we hope you will have a nice time . . . and be ever so happy . . . over in France."

How can I forget them now I am having a nice time, now that I am ever so happy over in France?

Besides, Pierre loves this photograph. He knows every girl by name—that is why the edges are so grubby. He pulls it out so often to study the queer English names written in strange English writing all over the back.

"Come on," he will say. "Tell me about this one again, this Pah-tree-cee-ah Ban-gal who went to the cookery class and put a saucepan on her head and couldn't get it off again."

Then I will tell him again about this Patricia Bingle and other shady characters I have met in Form 1C. And he tells me about the rip-roaring villains in his class at school—especially one Félix Numa who can spit like a cowboy and wears a real American belt as well as braces. But his Félix Numa went one better than my Pah-tree-cee-ah Ban-gal. He brought his father's false teeth to school to make the girls squeal. It seems they squealed all right. So did Félix Numa when his toothless papa caught up with him.

Oh yes, Pierre and I often spend a happy confidential half hour poring over the serried ranks of my last Form 1C.

On this next page I have a photograph that Mrs. Penny sent me just after Aunt Kate died.

"I'd like you to have it," she wrote, "to remind you of happy old times."

It is a photograph of Aunt Kate and Mrs. Penny leaning on our garden gate. I remember a persuasive gentleman came knocking at our door one summer day offering to take it for a shilling down and the other eighteenpence when delivered, handsomely mounted. I'm not in it. I was in bed with the mumps, worrying where my face left off and my neck began. And Aunt Kate used to say I might just as well have been in it, mumps and all, for it was a speaking likeness of our garden gate and the hollyhocks, but that was about all a Christian could say. At least she hoped it was.

Yet, I don't know. As I look at it, I can almost hear
Aunt Kate cracking one of her jokes, and Mrs. Penny's
warm chuckle.

Now here, on this page, I have a wedding group,
a double wedding, yes, Françoise's and mine. We decided
to make one "do" of it, and Françoise and Benoit came
down to Nîmes, and we were married, all four, on the
same day. No fuss, no ceremony, everything very quiet
and homely, our only guests—the regulars, and Monsieur
Tallon and his wife.

Monsieur Tallon took this photograph, of course.

There stands Marius in that brown tweed "costume-
sport" of his, yellow tie with red spots, his yellow shoes,
and holding his biscuit-coloured hat—just as he looked
that day in Lyons. I could tell that he really admired himself in this get-up, so I didn't have the heart to suggest
something a little more subdued. And very odd he looked,
too, by the side of Benoit Frécon. Now he turned up in
deepest black from head to toe, and smelling to heaven of
moth-balls. It seemed that he'd had to buy this "complete"
for his mother's funeral; and as she had always liked
everything of the best, honest Benoit had felt it his last
solemn duty to invest in the finest and blackest cloth his
tailor could offer him. Cost the earth it had. So Françoise
said he might as well get some wear out of it; and really
it looked quite distinguished, didn't it now, cheered up
with the smart grey bow-tie she'd bought him, and his
new patent-leather shoes and white buttonhole.

As for Françoise, she is wearing a smart brown
"trotter" which she also cheered up—with a frilly pink
blouse. And I treated myself to the "very latest shout in

navy-blue tailored robes", at least that is what the elegant young woman in black down at the Galeries Parisiennes swore it was, as she swept me into buying it.

"But it is absolutely you, Madame!" she declared. "But absolutely!"

Then in an unnecessary burst of candour, "So correct! So practical!"

By my side stands little Pierre, very stiff and proud in his new French sailor-suit with long trousers and a scarlet pom-pom on his hat—his own choice, indeed the only possible choice for any boy who desires to do his family credit at a wedding, I gathered.

Behind us stand the regulars, beaming away over their white buttonholes. Altogether we look as cheerful a crowd of middle-aged people as you could hope to meet. In the years to come, of course, Pierre will certainly grin, "Ah no! Name of a pipe! Don't you all look quaint!" But we won't mind. You can tell that by the look on our faces.

Strange though, when I think of it—my mother and I both marrying a Marius Durand, and both of them fancying themselves in a sporting wedding suit of stout British tweed.

Here, on this page, I have a small photograph of my cousin, Catherine, now travelling half round the world with Mrs. Luvisa Van Winkle. Across one corner Catherine has written: "A thousand affectionate thoughts from a sunny garden in beautiful Italy."

And Catherine is taking it easy in the sunny garden of beautiful Italy, reclining in what Marius calls a "Trans-atlantique de luxe"—a comfortable deck-chair, gay parasol over her head, looking very happy indeed, and a great deal plumper.

Oh yes, Catherine is having a wonderful time. She writes us the most interesting letters, and it is plain that she gets on famously with Mrs. Van Winkle. In every letter it is, "Mrs. Van Winkle says this," and, "Mrs. Van Winkle says that," and in the last one it was, "Luvisa thinks we may be able to fix a trip to Arabia as well."

And as Françoise says, this definitely casts no end of a lustre over the rest of the family as well. Not everyone can lean on their counter and say, "Had another letter from Catherine this morning. Riding on camels in the desert now if you please!"

And here, on this page, I have a photograph that I little dreamed I should ever see in my Family Album— one of myself, sitting outside the Café-Restaurant des Monuments de Nîmes. Monsieur Tallon's idea. In fact he absolutely insisted on taking it. He said he wanted to send a copy to his grandmama and Aunt Pélagie. And he took the utmost pains to arrange the tables and chairs to look precisely as they do in my old photograph— the photograph *his* grandpapa took of *my* grandpapa.

There I am, then, sitting just where my grandfather sat, just where I used to pretend to sit when I was a little girl and I had victoriously recited all my French home-work. And there on the wall behind me, it still says:

Marius Durand

CAFÉ-RESTAURANT DES MONUMENTS DE NÎMES
CHAMBRES POUR VOYAGEURS.

And the "Confort Moderne", too, of course.

But now on the window to my right, it says, in expensive gold letters:

> *English Spokken Hear*
> *Tea as in London.*

Marius had this done one day when I was out shopping —as a nice surprise.

It was. It still is, every time I look at it. And when English visitors pass by and spot it, they have a nice surprise, too; and often come in and request tea as in London to follow their steak and chips as in Nîmes.

Yes, there I am sitting outside the Café-Restaurant des Monuments de Nîmes, my grandfather's home, my father's home—and now—my home. And I think how Françoise said one day, "Home is where the heart is," and, well, my heart's right there.

Marius has, however, one little criticism to make of this photograph. He says it was a thousand pities he did not think of setting a bottle labelled "Best Rhubarb Wine" on the table before me, then we could have written across one corner, "Photograph of a dream come true."

On this next page I have another unusual photograph for a Family Album—a football team, every player jauntily spick and span, hair beautifully parted on gleaming head, arms folded across immaculate shirt; and a brand-new ball in the exact centre of the forward-line. The Scarlet Wolves, of course.

Pierre and I follow their matches with breathless interest

in the newspapers that Françoise sends us regularly from Saint Etienne.

"Ah, chic alors!" Pierre will crow. "We've won again! Seven–nil!"

If we lose, however, we not only strive to stifle our black suspicions of the referee, we also endeavour to say a gentlemanly "Hard luck!" as in the best sporting circles in Britain.

To our delight, a fortnight ago the Scarlet Wolves were playing the Sons of Provence in a village close by. We went, of course; cheered ourselves hoarse; and brought them all back to dinner. It was then that they presented me with this photograph, inscribed: "With respectful homage".

I have an uneasy feeling that they will never forget that I once watched Arsenal play.

On this next page I have a family group, the family with whom I travelled down to Nîmes—the Tardys. They always call in to see us when they are in Nîmes, and we often go to Saint Didier-of-the-Vines to spend a Sunday with them.

After lunch, Marius and Monsieur Tardy set to and thoroughly overhaul the government, world politics, the railways of France, and their stirring years in the army together, in the teeth of fearful odds and a camel of a sergeant-major, who, as Madame Tardy says, grows more and more of a hump every time they meet.

She and I listen for a while, and then slip away, unobserved, to the kitchen, to get on with the washing-up and other home affairs. Outside, through the open window, we can hear Pierre having the time of his life teaching all those girls this game of cricket, with an olive tree for a wicket, but a real British bat all the way from a shop in London. The girls, at the moment, just gallop for the ball, and gratefully take it in turns to bowl. Maybe later on Pierre will consider allowing them to have a go with his bat. But he is making no promises. It all depends on how they shape.

In this photograph all five girls are wearing tartan dresses, very French tartan, with white hand-embroidered collars and cuffs, very long white hand-knitted socks, and white shoes. They are standing in a line, in order of size, right hand on the shoulder in front, and bringing up the rear, Maman and Papa—looking very proud, as well they might, especially Maman. She and the girls made every stitch they are wearing—except Papa's suit, of course. Monsieur Pinatel made that.

And as I look at Maman's smiling face, I think indignantly of the arrant nonsense so often talked and written about French women by people who can never have set foot in a real French home.

As Marius says, there are a million Madame Tardys in France to every one Lady of the Camellias. He says there always have been; but they are far too busy to be vocal outside the home, so nobody ever notices them much, not even in France.

Marius says . . . How easily I write of all he says, and how hard I find it to tell of all he means to me, of all we mean to each other. Oh, I am not pretending that it is anything like the sharp wild passion of which poets sing. It is far more comfortable, thank God, and kind. And, in its own way, very dear and lovely.

I know this. I wouldn't change places with any woman, not for all the tea in China. Even when made as in London.

But I must hurry on, for here glowering at me from this next daisy-decked page of my Family Album, is a bouncing baby, a British baby. And the look on her face suggests she has no patience with all this dilly-dallying—especially when a girl has next to nothing on.

Maybe you remember that a young couple called Stevens took over our house when I left for France. Well, this is their baby.

And young Mrs. Stevens did so want me to see what a fine child she was—not fat, mind you, just a shade over-weight, that was all—that she had her taken in her little vest, kicking her heels up on a pillow, displaying all her curves and dimples; and looking remarkably like my father at ten months on the very first page of my Family Album.

And I can almost hear that fine British baby in the years to come: "Mummy! Fancy having me taken like that! Don't you dare show it when Susan So-and-so comes to tea!"

Her name, by the way, is Dorothy—after me. I little thought I should ever be paid such a compliment, I can tell you. And young Mrs. Stevens and I are already planning long holidays for her with us in France so that she may learn to talk like a native. And later on we shall certainly send Pierre to spend a few months with them, so that he, too, may learn to talk like a native.

He has already made a start. He understands a sur-prising amount of my "conversation for young beginners" especially if I hint at a treat of some sort. But at his age a boy is far too busy, of course, to answer back in a slow foreign tongue. So when he loses his smart English school-satchel, which he does twice daily, I say, for instance, "Have . . . you . . . looked . . . in . . . the . . . kitchen?" And he shrieks, "Ah! La cuisine!" and gallops there to get it.

And he doesn't call me "Maman". Oh no! When he comes home from school, he pushes aside the bead curtains in our doorway, and yells, "Mum! Oo-oo! Mum!"

Then he turns to the thirsty young friends he has brought home with him, and swaggers, "English! That's what English kids bawl! She talks it, easy as easy, just like that. Me, I talk it, too. Listen!"

"Mum! Mum! Please, we 'ave some lee-moan-ahde, no? Yes, please, yes?"

I often think how Aunt Kate would have loved him. As I do. A woman does not always have to give birth to a child to love him with all her heart.

Indeed now, when I look at my Family Album, I am very glad that there are still a number of empty, waiting spaces—spaces that I shall fill, please God.

This space, for instance, with Easter lilies on either side, is reserved for the photograph that Monsieur Tallon will take of Pierre the day he makes his First Holy Communion, a very special day in a French child's life.

"It is different from all other days," Marius once told me. "I am not one for chest-thumping, but I tell you this day has a strange atmosphere of innocence and, yes, goodness. Up there in His heaven, the good God Himself and all the saints, haloes very bright for the occasion, and Papa and Maman and everybody else one knows on Earth, are all, all, very moved to see a child looking and feeling so spotless and good. And so very well-dressed. Also a child knows that the presents he will get may not all turn out to be further aids to piety. No, no, they may well include a luminous watch for a deserving boy, or a beautiful bangle for a dear little girl.

"And certainly, oh, most certainly, there will be nothing short of a banquet at home, at which this child sits, the guest of honour, a little white and remote maybe, because of all this goodness swirling about him catching at his throat. And a little stiff, too, of course, in such fine beautiful clothes.

"But a day to remember all one's life! The only day when heaven and earth both stop all they are doing to embrace a child who has tried very hard to be good."

This next page is booked, too. On it I have solemnly vowed to glue the large photograph Pierre will have taken for me on the day he becomes Admiral of the French Fleet. It will be taken on his flagship, of course, ship's company saluting in the respectful background, all hand-picked men, and very proud to be sailing under their new admiral on the finest and fastest ship that ever weighed anchor in Brest or Toulon.

We have not yet, however, come to a firm decision on her name. At the moment we are torn between *Invincible* and *Cyclone de Nîmes*.

At the moment, too, we are very much aware that Christmas is drawing very near. Pierre is so dramatically polite and well-behaved. So are all his friends, even that tough guy, Félix Numa, the one who can spit like a cow-boy. He only spits now to oblige the others, and never, never when unappreciative adults are in sight.

They are all out to touch our hearts for a few francs to buy something we never see in England—little figures a few inches high, made of baked clay, and painted the most vivid of colours, blue, red, green and yellow. Every sweetshop, every stationer, seems to be showing whole collections of these little figures—santons, they call them.

There is always Saint Joseph, very homely, in brown, with a white lily in his hand; the Blessed Virgin in blue bespangled with stars; a jocund Baby with rosy cheeks and yellow curly hair; a little manger just His size; a patient donkey to stand by His side, and an ox, and a white woolly lamb.

Then there is quite a celestial choice of little clay angels in the brightest of robes and the whitest of wings, and shepherds wrapped in their cloaks carrying little lambs on their shoulders.

But that is not all. Once he has all these, every child goes on to collect other santons of all the good people of old Provence. He must have Monsieur the Mayor in a tall hat and red, white and blue sash about his waist; a drummer with sticks and a very tall drum; a fish wife with her scales and basket of fish; a milkmaid with her measure and pail of milk; a poor peasant with the finest of cabbages under his arm. All these he simply must have; and many, many others as well, all dressed in the gay costumes of long-ago.

And the children carry home their new santons as

if they were rare jewels—as indeed they are; and as they pass by we often hear snatches of brisk bartering:

"Now listen! I've got two Lord Mayors. So I'll swop this one for a good donkey. But with all four legs, mind!"

Tonight, before he went to bed, Pierre and I cleared the top of the chest of drawers in his room; and on it, with four rolls of cottonwool, we set up the hills and valleys of Palestine. We put jagged stones here and there to make rocks and boulders; and between them we stuck the little trees we had made of green and brown paper.

Then down every hill we made twisting paths of fine silver sand, with a tree here and there to make a welcome shade.

Behind all this, and leaning against the wall, we carefully placed a large sheet of blue paper for the sky; one silver star high on it, a very large star, that Pierre can see as he lies in bed.

And Pierre, dark eyes very soft and gentle, set down the stable he had made of brown cardboard; and put in his little manger and filled it with tiny wisps of straw. And on it, he laid his Baby.

Then all about the manger he set His Mother and Saint Joseph, and the ox and the lamb and the patient donkey; and behind them the shepherds carrying their lambs.

On the roof of his stable he set all his angels, every one; and coming down the silver paths he set his other santons, all the good people of old Provence hurrying down to Bethlehem, rejoicing.

Then he stood back and looked at all this.

"There!" he said. "There! On that high hill at the back. That's where it must go!"

He ran through the door. And came back . . . with the china house, the little china house I loved so dearly when I was a child.

And he carefully flattened the top of the highest cottonwool hill, and set it upon it. Then from his pocket he pulled out my torch, and ran to the door and turned off the light.

"Now!" he said. "Now!"

I fixed the torch behind the china house and switched it on.

And instantly a gentle light shone through the windows and lit up all our Palestine.

Pierre caught my hand and held it tight. And, looking down, I saw his face.

And oh, it was as if every little angel had spread his shining wings and cried, "Gloria! Gloria!"